Paleoanthropology and Primate Evolution

ELEMENTS OF ANTHROPOLOGY
A Series of Introductions

Paleoanthropology and Primate Evolution

James A. Gavan
University of Missouri

WM. C. BROWN COMPANY PUBLISHERS
Dubuque, Iowa

ANTHROPOLOGY SERIES

Consulting Editors

Frank Johnson
University of Pennsylvania

Henry Selby
Temple University

Library of Congress Catalog Card Number: 76-11976

ISBN 0–697–07524–9

Printed in the United States of America

To My Margaret

Contents

Preface

Paleoanthropology is really a new branch of anthropology even though the name means "old anthropology." Certainly neither the study of anthropology nor the study of primate fossils is new. But it is only within recent years that these two fields have converged to the point where an understanding of modern man's complexity requires an understanding of the evolutionary course by which man came to dominate the world. Perhaps this point of view was best expressed by one of the founders of American physical anthropology, Earnest A. Hooton, when he wrote "If we are to understand man, if we are to be anthropologists in a real sense of the term, our knowledge of every aspect of the human organism and its functioning should extend downward to its lower primate origin."[1]

The two faces of man—his biology and his culture—are today so interwoven that each exerts an influence on the other. But his biology came first, although it was not always as it is now. If we are to understand the complexity of modern peoples, one foundation must be human biological history. That history, as we move to the past, quickly becomes intimately intertwined with that of our close taxonomic relatives, the primates. All of the intricacies of that history cannot be presented here, but I have attempted to provide a brief introduction to it. Evidence for primate evolution will be shown, while at the same time giving you some idea of the numerous remaining problems. Certainly we have much to learn about both our human and our nonhuman ancestors.

I sincerely hope that this brief introduction to paleoanthropology will provide a basis for the equally fascinating study of anthropology itself.

James A. Gavan
Columbia, Missouri

1. E. A. Hooton, "The importance of primate studies in Anthropology," in *The Non-Human Primates and Human Evolution,* ed. J. A. Gavan (Detroit: Wayne University Press (1955), p. 9.

1 The Contemporary Primates

THE ORDER PRIMATES

The contemporary primates are a fairly variable group of relatively unspecialized mammals who, because of their close relation to man, are of special interest to anthropologists. To understand their fossil history, we must know the end product of that phylogenetic development. Therefore we will briefly review the extant members before introducing the fossil evidence for primate evolution.

Their relatively unspecialized morphology has made it difficult to provide a formal definition of the Order. The best dictionary-type definition was provided by Mivart, who said that primates are:

> . . . unguiculate, claviculate placental mammals, with orbits encircled by bone; three kinds of teeth, at least at one time of life; brain always with a posterior lobe and calcarine fissure; the innermost digit of at least one pair of extremities opposable; hallux with a flat nail or none; a well-developed caecum; penis pendulous; testes scrotal; always two pectoral mammae.[1]

No one trait separates the Order Primates from all other mammalian Orders, but taken as a group the above traits serve very well as long as only contemporary forms are considered. If we are to trace the phylogenetic history of this Order, however, many of the traits listed by Mivart are unusable. In general, features confined to soft tissue, such as brain morphology, will be imperfectly preserved or absent in the fossil record. Because the skeleton is the most likely preserved part, it would seem best to emphasize skeletal traits of the Order. But in so doing the student should be aware that selection is the primary force in evolution; and that selection operates on the totality of form, function, and behavior. Therefore, in studying the skeleton we are not necessarily directly studying traits that adapt these animals to their ecological niche. Some traits of the skeleton directly reflect a successful adaptation; other traits are probably no more than an indirect measure; and in still other cases the traits are so trivial it is difficult to see what selective advantage could accrue from them. Such features, however, can be used to assess relations among forms; that is, can be used to establish a phylogenetic classification.

In considering the skeleton, remember that all Primates are in the Class Mammalia and that the mammalian skeleton is adapted for agile living on land. In general, the Order Primates has retained many skeletal features of primitive mammals but has modified these features in the direction of ar-

1. S. Mivart, "On *Lepilemur* and *Cheirogaleus* and on the zoological rank of Lemuroides," *Proceedings of the Zoological Society of London* (1873), p. 507.

boreal living. Just as all mammals have not remained on the land, so too, not all Primates have remained in the trees. Yet primate anatomy can be understood only in a context of adaptation to an arboreal niche. (See Glossary for a definition of all anatomical terms in this book.)

ADAPTATION AND SPECIALIZATION

The entire process of adaptation implies that preexisting structures are modified to permit a new way of life, but the new mode is always a modification of the old. Adaptation has produced drastic modifications in some forms, while others retain many features of the common ancestor. A general tendency exists in the case of those making drastic modifications to become highly specialized to a very specific way of life. Those making fewer modifications retain greater flexibility in the way they exploit their environment. Most contemporary primates belong to the second category. The primate adaptation to arboreal living was accomplished with comparatively little modification of a basic mammalian pattern.

Probably the one great specialization has been the elaboration of the brain and the concomitant ability to learn. Mivart refers to this in his definition when he points out that primates have a brain with a posterior lobe and a calcarine fissure. Even in the most undifferentiated of the primates, the brain shows a complexity not found in most other mammals; in the primates this complexity reaches its highest expression. The result is that specific behaviors are the result of learning and very little is due to genetic endowment. Unfortunately, this great primate achievement is only imperfectly preserved in the fossil record.

Other characteristics listed by Mivart but not preserved in the fossil record are "a well-developed caecum; penis pendulous; testes scrotal; always two pectoral mammae." Since these are soft tissue features, they will not be discussed here.

Primates as a group have some common morphological features associated with life in the trees, even though not all present-day primates live in trees nor do arboreal ones exploit the trees in exactly the same way. One of these common features is the possession of grasping extremities; that is, the primate exploits trees by grasping a tree limb rather than by digging claws into it. There is an evolutionary tendency for primates to lose claws and replace them with flat nails (they are *unguiculate*—have claws or nails—in Mivart's definition). Thus all primates have at least one flat nail on each extremity. Another aspect of the grasping complex is the development of ridges of skin on the palms, soles, and digits. Sweat glands are arranged along these ridges (often referred to as fingerprints but more properly called dermatoglyphics). These ridges provide friction between the hands and feet and the tree limb, thus helping to prevent slipping.

ARBOREAL ADAPTATION IN THE EXTREMITIES

When moving through the trees the primate may grasp a higher or lower limb. To do this it needs a highly flexible upper extremity. This is achieved by retaining the maximum degrees of motion at the various joints of the extremity. Most running mammals only use their upper extremities in a fore and aft motion. That is, the shoulder joint permits only flexion-extension; primates on the other hand have retained the original three degrees of motion at this joint. They not only can flex and extend, but they can also abduct-adduct (move the extremity away from the center of the body and back towards it), as well as rotate the entire extremity. These three degrees of motion are very important for any animal that must reach either above its head or out to the side to grasp a randomly-oriented limb.

Another aspect of this flexibility of motion is found in the forearm. Primates retain two bones in the forearm—the radius and ulna. These are arranged so that the distal (lower) end of the radius can rotate around the ulna. That is, the bones may be parallel or crossed. If the elbow is bent so that the forearm is at a right angle to the arm and if the palm of the hand is up, these two bones will be parallel. When the palm is turned down the bones are crossed. This ability permits the motion of supination-pronation in the forearm. The combination of this forearm motion with rotation at the shoulder permits the hand to rotate almost 360 degrees. Bone arrangement in the wrist also permits a wide range of motion at that joint.

In addition, the entire upper extremity can be moved because it is attached to the scapula (shoulder blade), which in turn has a wide range of motion across the posterior trunk. This highly flexible upper extremity has bony contact with the trunk only through the clavicle (collar bone), a strut to help stabilize the shoulder on the lateral aspect of the trunk. Thus in Mivart's definition, primates are claviculate mammals.

Most mammals, especially the fast runners, have sacrificed upper-extremity mobility for stability through the loss of a functional clavicle and an independently movable radius and ulna. Many have also lost some wrist and digit bones. By contrast, the primates have achieved a highly flexible upper extremity by retaining the primitive vertebrate pattern of bones in almost its original condition. The detailed morphology of these bones has changed, and the range of motion has been increased, but the pattern of bony relations is a premammalian heritage.

In all mammals the lower extremity is more stable than the upper because it must propel the animal forward. The pelvic girdle, considerably less flexible than the pectoral girdle, consists of three bones, an *os coxae* on each side joined together posteriorly by the sacrum. There is little motion permitted at the joints between the sacrum and each *os coxae* or between the two *os coxae* where they meet anteriorly. This entire structure has been stabilized to transmit force between the trunk and lower extremity. Although the primate pelvic girdle follows this basic pattern of all mammals, the lower extremity itself has considerable flexibility. The motions of flexion-extension, abduction-adduction, and rotation are all possible at the hip joint, but in the leg the fibula cannot rotate on the tibia thus preventing any motion comparable to the forearm's pronation-supination. The primate ankle joint permits a wide range of motion although not to the extent found at the wrist. The primate foot has five digits and the innermost, the hallux, is opposable to the other digits in all except man. Thus in the hands and feet primates have retained five digits; they are characterized by pentadactylism. Most other mammals have lost at least some of these digits.

In general, the primate extremities have retained the primitive vertebrate pattern of bones, modified only to the extent of permitting a high degree of flexibility. This flexibility is adaptive in terms of the way in which the primates have exploited their arboreal habitat.

One characteristic of arboreal mammals is their tendency to sit vertically and to bring food to the mouth with their upper extremities. Part of this behavior complex results in the ability of all primates to walk on their lower extremities. This is not to say that all are bipedal, but all will so walk under the proper circumstances. The tendency toward holding the trunk vertical is at least partially responsible for a reorientation of the face with respect to the cranium. In most mammals the face projects anteriorly in front of the cranium, but in primates the face is, to some extent, rotated back under the cranium. The exact degree of this reorientation differs in the various primate groups. Associated with this change in face orientation is a change in the position of the foramen magnum, the large hole in the base of the skull through which the spinal cord passes. In most terrestrial mammals the foramen magnum is located at the rear of the cranium, but in primates it has moved forward under the cranium. Again the degree of forward shift differs in the various groups.

SIGHT REORIENTATION

In hunted animals the orbits tend to be situated on the side of the head so that the animal has as wide a range of vision as possible. Hunting and arboreal animals have orbits situated in the front, enabling these animals to judge distance more accurately. For an animal to jump open space and grasp a distant limb, it must be able to judge accurately the distance to that limb. Accurate estimation of distance is achieved through the perfection of stereoscopic vision, that is, by having a large overlap in the fields of vision of the two eyes. To accomplish this the orbits move to a frontal plane. However, when this position of the primate eye is coupled with the tendency for the face to move down and under the cranium, the large temporalis muscles come in close proximity to each eyeball. The temporalis muscle arises on the side of the head and inserts on the mandible; it is one of the main muscles for closing the jaws. If this muscle were to exert pressure on the eyeball, it could cause permanent damage. This condition is at least partially prevented by extensions from the frontal and the zygomatic bones so that a bony lateral rim is formed about the orbit. Mivart refers to this condition by saying ". . . with orbits encircled by bone."

As the orbits move frontally over the course of time (and thus come closer together), the area available to the nose lessens. Primates hence became eye-oriented mammals at the expense of their sense of smell. This is not only reflected in the reduced nasal portion of the primate skull but also in the reduced size of the brain areas associated with smell. The areas of the brain associated with vision concomitantly increased.

OTHER PRIMATE TRAITS

The general morphology of most primate teeth is suited to an omnivorous diet. With some notable exceptions the teeth of primates are low crowned with blunt cusps on the cheek teeth. Contemporary primates all lack at least one incisor and one premolar once present in primitive mammals. Thus no primate has a dental formula greater than 2.1.3.3/2.1.3.3 = 36. This formula is read as two incisors, one canine, three premolars, and three molars in both the upper and lower jaws. Because the sides of the mouth are symmetrical, the sum of these numbers must be doubled to obtain the total number of teeth. Many primate groups, however, have a reduced number of teeth.

In following the primates backward through geologic time, we can expect to note that the ancestors will have fewer and fewer traits typical of extant forms and come to resemble some form now considered to be a nonprimate. Because all must ultimately trace back to some kind of common ancestor, it is apparent that the definition of the earliest primates must be made on some arbitrary basis. Surprisingly, many paleontologists are agreeing that the structure of the middle ear is the single trait to use in arbitrarily separating the earliest primates from nonprimates. Why the precise structure of this difficult-to-observe region should confer any selective advantage on the animals possessing it is not yet apparent, but as a classificatory device it is useful.

The middle ear lies within the temporal bone, a bone on the side of the head into which the tube of the external ear passes. The temporal bone has a complex history both from the phylogenetic (evolutionary) and from the ontogenetic points of view. (Ontogeny is the growth of the individual from conception to senescence.) The temporal bone has two main parts. The first, the squamosal portion, forms a part of the side of the cranium; the second, or petrosal portion, forms a part of the skull base. In addition, ontogenetically separate bones contribute to the lateral extension that encompasses the external auditory meatus (ear hole). This tubular portion of the external ear is closed internally by the tympanic membrane (eardrum). Immediately internal to the tympanic membrane is an incompletely closed cavity—the middle ear—which communicates with the throat via the eustachian tube. The floor of the cavity is made of bone. In primates the bony floor of the middle ear is formed entirely by the petrous portion of the temporal bone (fig. 1.1). In some primates the floor may be greatly expanded inferiorly to form a bulla. In nonprimate mammals bones other than the petrosal contribute to the formation of the bulla.

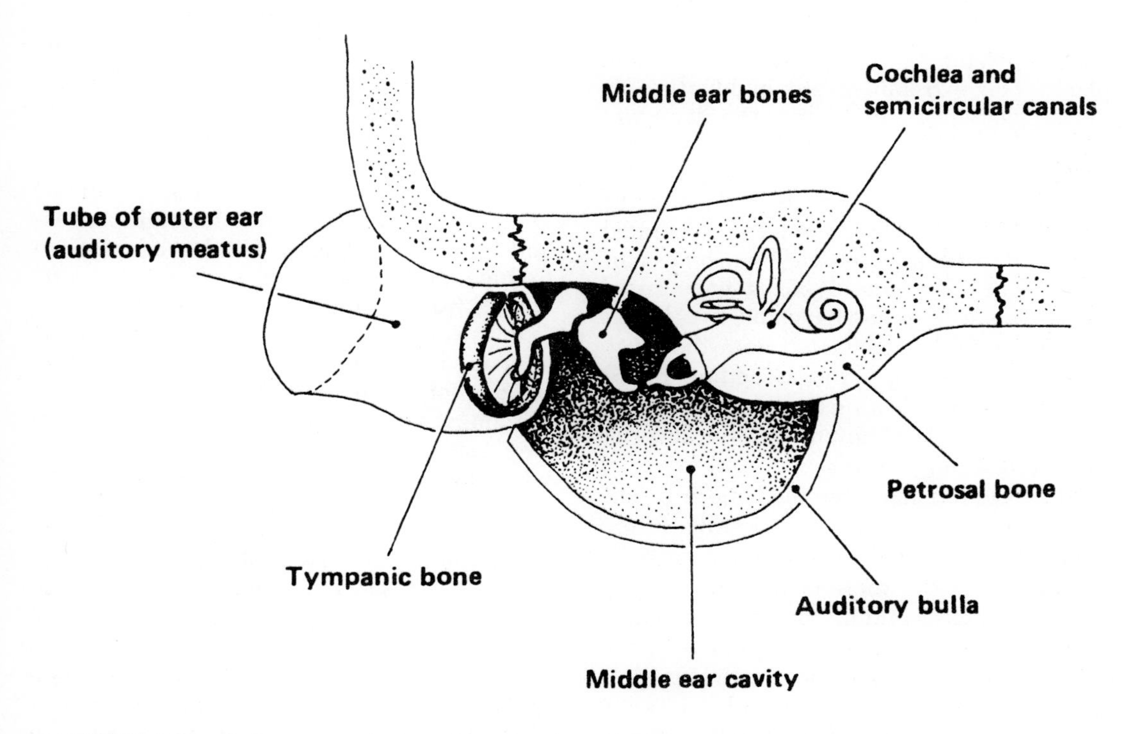

FIGURE 1.1. A diagrammatic frontal section through the temporal bone showing the structure of the middle ear. (From Matt Cartmill, 1975 **Primate Origins,** Burgess Publishing Company. Reprinted by permission.)

SUBDIVISIONS OF THE ORDER—PROSIMIANS AND ANTHROPOIDS

The Order Primates may be subdivided into two very distinct groups, or Suborders. The first, the Anthropoidea, includes not only man but also the great apes and the monkeys. From an ethnocentric point of view we often consider these the higher primates, whereas the other Suborder, the Prosimii, are considered lower primates. The Anthropoidea, however, are higher only in the sense that they have deviated more from the common ancestor, but it would be inaccurate to conclude that the Prosimii are unsuccessful in an evolutionary sense.

In general, the Anthropoidea show a perfecting of the primate mode of exploiting the arboreal niche. All digits now have nails; the sense of smell is greatly reduced; and the orbits are oriented in a frontal plane. The extremities are highly flexible grasping organs, and sight is the dominant sense. Skeletally, these changes are best reflected in the skull and mandible. The face is more rotated under the cranium, and the orbital cavity is now completely separated from the temporalis muscle by a bony partition. The two frontal bones have fused into a single bone, as have the two halves of the mandible. Associated with the reorientation of the face, the ascending ramus of the mandible has increased in length so that the condyle is now above the level of the teeth.

The Prosimii have retained more of the early primate features. There is still a suture between the two halves of the mandible indicating that the incisors are still merely grasping devices and are not used in biting. A metopic suture is retained between the two frontal bones, and a complete bony partition does not separate the orbital cavity from the temporalis muscle. Smell is still an important sense as these animals retain a rhinarium (wet nose) like that of a dog or cat. Like many other mammals they also retain vibrissae (sensory hairs on the face).

Among the Anthropoidea the anterior dentition is very conservative. That is, they retain two incisors and one canine on each side of each jaw. Further, there is very little modification in the structure of these teeth, especially the incisors. Among the Prosimii, however, the form of these teeth has not only been modified but teeth have been lost in some genera. In most present-day Prosimii, the lower incisors and canines have become procumbent, that is, compressed laterally and extended anteriorly, and thus cannot articulate with the teeth of the upper jaw. This combination of six anterior teeth (two incisors and one canine on each side of the mandible) form a "dental comb" that the animals use in grooming.

Man, an Anthropoid

Man, a member of the Anthropoidea, is most closely allied with the apes. To this group belong the gibbon, siamang, and orangutan of South Asia, and the chimpanzee and gorilla of Africa. In the adaptation to bipedal locomotion man has been left with a freed upper extremity and a modified lower one, but the above-mentioned animals have moved in the direction of brachiation—locomotion by swinging under the limbs. This locomotor adaptation places emphasis upon the upper extremity because when swinging through the trees the lower extremity does not bear weight. The gibbons and siamangs have carried this adaptation to its highest degree probably because of their small body size. The others are now too heavy to be really agile in the trees.

Although his locomotion differs, man shares certain skeletal traits with the apes. All lack a tail, possess a short lumbar region of the trunk, and have a broad and shallow thoracic region. The permanent dental formula is $2.1.2.3/2.1.2.3 = 32$, and the molars show the so-called dryopithecine cusp pattern (fig. 1.2).

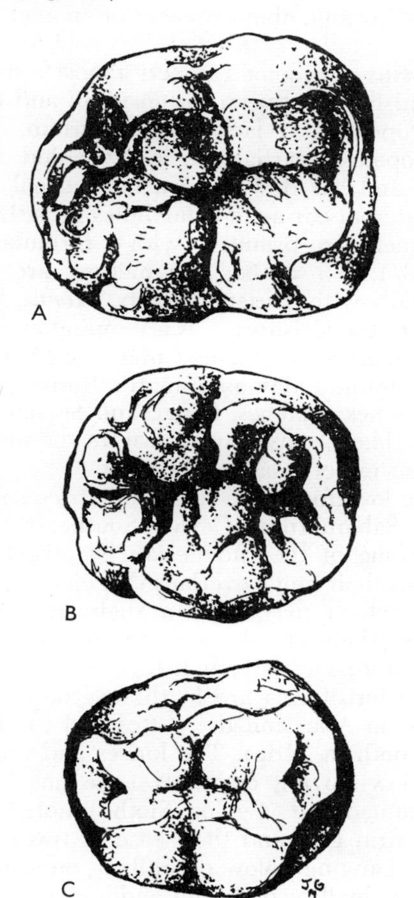

FIGURE 1.2. The molar cusp pattern in some catarrhines. A and B are examples of the dryopithecine pattern; C is an example of the bilophodont patter. (A = **Dryopithecus**, B = **Homo**, and C = **Macaca**)

Most apes show sexual dimorphism, with the male being considerably larger than the female. The chimpanzee and gibbon show the least dimorphic development among the apes. Dentally, sexual dimorphism is reflected in the large tusk-like canine of the male. The canine projects beyond the level of the other teeth and, when the jaws are closed, the upper canine fits into a diastema (gap) in the lower tooth row between the lower canine and the anterior premolar. The lower canine fits into a similar gap in the upper jaw between the canine and lateral incisor. The sharp, posterior edge of the upper canine hones against the front sharp edge on the lower, anterior premolar. The anterior teeth, incisors and canines, are arranged almost straight across the jaws while the posterior teeth extend back in parallel rows. The palate is thus U-shaped with the canines at the corners.

The arrangement of human teeth differs from those of man's close relatives. The canines are no longer than the other teeth; no diastema exists in either jaw. The lower anterior premolar is bicuspid; that is, it has two cusps and is used for grinding rather than shearing. The palate is arcuate with no sharp corner at the canine. Man's face is almost completely under the cranium; he lacks facial prognathism.

Monkeys, Anthropoids Too

The Suborder Anthropoidea also includes the monkeys—Old World and New World groups. The Old World monkeys, or cercopithecoids, are similar to man and the apes in that they have the same dental formula and bony external auditory meatus. Unlike the apes, they have a tail of varying length, a long lumbar region, and a narrow, deep thorax. Fittingly, cercopithecoids are basically quadrupedal animals who exploit the trees by running on top of the limbs.

The cercopithecoid canine is a long tooth, much narrower than in apes. As in the apes, however, the upper canine shears against the anterior, lower premolar. Also, there is a diastema in both jaws, and the posterior tooth rows are parallel. Instead of the dryopithecine cusp pattern, cercopithecoids have a bilophodont molar (fig. 1.2). This consists of four cusps with the anterior two and the posterior two cusps connected by a loph (crest of enamel).

The cercopithecoids are divided into two groups; the mainly Asian colobines, and the mainly African cercopithecines. However, one Genus of colobines, *Colobus*, is found in Africa, and one Genus of cercopithecines, *Macaca*, is not only found in Asia but is also found on the Rock of Gibraltar and adjacent portions of North Africa. *Macaca* is the only nonhuman primate found in Europe today. In Asia the Genus *Macaca* extends all the way from India to the northern islands of Japan and a small portion of the adjacent mainland.

The Old World monkeys are a pretty successful group, having adapted to a wide variety of physical environments. Some of them, the baboons, virtually abandoned the trees and became savannah dwellers.

The New World monkeys, or platyrrhines, are not as diversified as their Old World cousins. They are restricted to the tropics and none has become terrestrial. Unlike the other Anthropoidea, they retain an additional premolar so that in most the formula is 2.1.3.3/2.1.3.3 = 36 (one group has lost the third molars and thus has 32 teeth). In addition, the external auditory canal is cartilaginous like that of most Prosimii (fig. 1.3).

Some, but not all, platyrrhines have developed a prehensile tail. Thus the only monkeys who can hang by their tails are in the New World.

The Prosimians

The Prosimii have differentiated into three groups: the lemuriforms, the lorisiforms, and the Genus *Tarsius*. *Tarsius* and the lorises are small animals, strictly arboreal and nocturnal. Some of the lemurs are nocturnal, and some of the diurnal ones are semiterrestrial. These latter are the largest of the Prosimii, about the size of an average dog.

Tarsius is in some respects almost a transitional form between the Prosimii and the Anthropoidea. It lacks the rhinarium, has developed a partial partition behind the orbit, and has developed a bony canal for the external ear as in catarrhines (fig. 1.3). The teeth are primitive with a formula of 2.1.3.3/1.1.3.3 = 34; the incisors are set vertically with no dental comb. *Tarsius*, like some of the lorisiforms, is a jumping animal with an elongated tarsus (ankle bone). *Tarsius* is found today on Sumatra, Borneo, the Philippines, Celebes, Sangi, and Salajar Islands. The Genus is unknown on the mainland of either Asia or Africa.

The lorisiforms are found in Africa south of the Sahara, India, Ceylon, Southeast Asia, and some of the Indonesian Islands. Like *Tarsius* their range overlaps that of the monkeys, which may explain their nocturnal habits (there is only one nocturnal anthropoid, *Aotus*, a platyrrhine).

The lorisiforms are in three groups, the lorises in Asia, and the pottos and the galagos both in Africa. The lorises and pottos are slow-moving creatures (one has been nicknamed the "Ceylon Sloth") noted for their firm grip and their ease of travelling while hanging below or walking on a limb. With a small second digit and a long fourth one, they produce a powerful grip between the first and fourth digits.

Galagos are active, jumping animals, and like *Tarsius* have an elongated ankle. They possess a long, bushy tail and a weaker grip than that of lorises and pottos. The lorisiforms and lemuriforms like the platyrrhines have a cartilaginous external-ear canal.

The third group of Prosimii, the lemuriforms, are restricted to Madagascar and the Comoro Islands, where they are not in com-

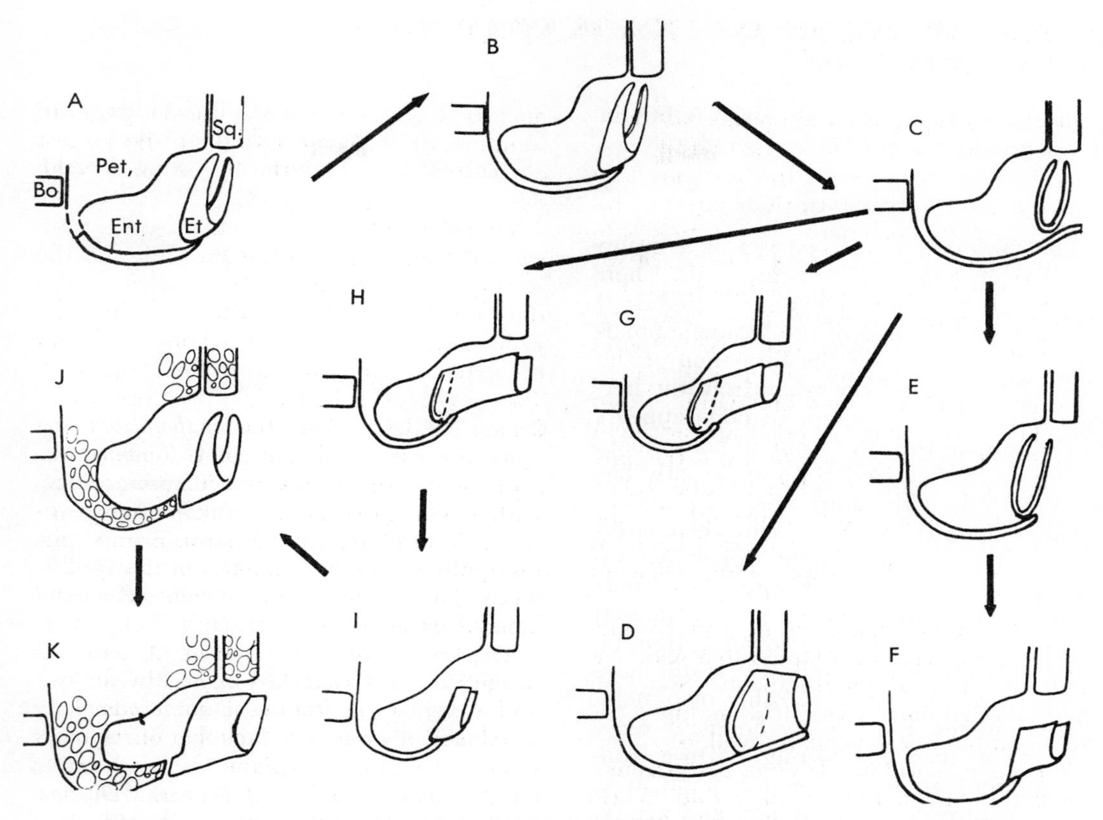

FIGURE 1.3. Variations in the structure of the middle ear in Primates. Arrows indicate possible developmental series according to Szalay. A—Hypothetical eutherian morphotype; B—Hypothetical intermediate between Primate and primitive eutherian morphotypes; C—Ancestral Primate pattern represented by Lemuriformes; D—**Megaladapis;** E—**Galago;** F—**Loris;** G—Paromomyidae; H—Tarsiidormes; I—**Tarsius,** a specialized Tarsiiformes; J—Platyrrhini; K—Catarrhini. (From Szalay, F. S. 1975 Primate phylogeny: The basicranial evidence, in: Luckett, W. P. and F. S. Szalay (Eds.) **Phylogeny of the Primates.** Plenum Publishing Corporation. Reprinted by permission.)

petition with other primates. The lemuriforms thus contain the only diurnal prosimians, a highly variable group with some becoming very aberrant. The most aberrant is probably the little aye-aye who has become so rodentlike that even the pulp cavity of its incisors remains open so that these teeth are continuously growing. The aye-aye's dental formula has been reduced to 1.0.1.3/1.0.0.3; the complete loss of the canine tooth being most unusual for a primate.

Among the other lemuriforms, size ranges from that of a rat to that of a fair-sized dog. All have the anterior dental comb and most have a dental formula of 2.1.3.3/2.1.3.3, as the platyrrhines. In most the upper extremity is shorter than the lower, although there is no jumping adaptation such as found in *Tarsius* or the galagos. An interesting feature among the family Indriidae is the possession of two instead of three premolars. This loss is apparently quite independent of the similar loss among the Anthropoidea. Also in this lemuriform family the lower canine is lost, leaving only thirty teeth in the permanent dentition.

SUMMARY

The Order Primates consists of a group of relatively unspecialized mammals. Their adaptation to arboreal living has required minimal modification of the basic mammalian pattern. However, the formation of the floor of the middle ear solely from the petrosal portion of the temporal bone appears to separate all Primates from all nonprimate mammals. But this criterion apparently has nothing to do with an arboreal adaptation.

Contemporary primates show characteristics of arboreal living: the upper extremity is an extremely flexible appendage, possessing wide ranges and degrees of motion at the various joints; the lower extremity, constructed for greater stability, is still more flexible than that of many other mammals.

In Primates, the eye is the main sense organ. The eyes tend to migrate to a frontal position, impinging on the nasal area, which in turn decreases in size and acuity. The face tends to become smaller in relation to the cranium and recede inferiorly. To protect the eye from pressure of the temporalis muscle, a bony ring encircles the orbit.

The Order Primates is divided into two Suborders, the Anthropoidea and the Prosimii. The latter has retained more features resembling the Order Insectivora than has the former. Although all primates are basically arboreal, not all exploit the trees in the same fashion. And though man is not the only primate to forsake the trees, he is the least arboreal primate.

Classification of taxa discussed in chapter 1:

Order: Primates
- Suborder: Anthropoidea
  - Infraorder: Catarrhini (Old World primates)
    - Superfamily: Hominoidea (man and apes)
    - Cercopithecoidea (Old World monkeys)
  - Infraorder: Platyrrhini (New World monkeys)
- Suborder: Prosimii
  - Infraorder: Tarsiiformes
    - Lorisiformes
    - Lemuriformes

For Further Reading

Gavan, J. A. *A Classification of the Order Primates,* Museum Briefs no. 16. Columbia, Mo.: Univ. of Missouri/Museum of Anthropology. A summary of the skeletal morphology associated with the taxa of contemporary primates. Useful for all chapters of this book.

Hill, W. C. O. *Primates: Comparative Anatomy and Taxonomy.* Vol. 1-8. New York: Interscience Publishers, 1953-1974. A series of eight volumes published over a twenty-one year period; it features a most complete, technical discussion of the topic. Its volumes are pertinent to all chapters in this book.

Jolly, A. *The Evolution of Primate Behavior.* The Macmillan Series in Physical Anthropology. New York: Macmillan Co., 1972. This is a nice review of primate ethology, a subject not considered in this book.

Watts, E. S. *Biology of the Living Primates.* Anthropology Series. Dubuque, Iowa: Wm. C. Brown Co. Publishers, 1975. A concise review of the contemporary members of the order Primates.

Bibliography

Mivart, S. 1873. "On *Lepilemur* and *Cheirogaleus* and on the zoological rank of Lemuroides." *Proceedings of the Zoological Society London,* pp. 484-510.

Szalay, F. S. 1972. "Cranial morphology of the early tertiary *Phenacolemur* and its bearing on primate phylogeny." *American Journal of Physical Anthropology* 36:59-76.

2 Geologic Time

Study of the phylogeny of any group requires a time scale to orient the fossil record. Contemporary historical research relies on the Gregorian calendar, but it is not presently adequate to date the earliest fossils. Thus their dating in terms of years is still incomplete.

GEOLOGIC TIME SCALE

In the early phases of the study of earth history, geologists established a relative scale to record the antiquity of an event. As geology matured names were assigned to definable time spans and eventually the present geologic time scale came into general use (table 2.1). According to this scheme, time was divided into a number of major divisions—eras. In the earliest of these no fossils were found (recent evidence, however, indicates the presence of microorganisms during that early time). The very earliest times are lumped into the Precambrian because multicellular animals with easily preserved hard parts are unknown at that time. The first era of any concern is the

TABLE 2.1. ERAS OF THE GEOLOGIC TIME SCALE

Era	Approximate number of years since beginning of era	Representative animals
Cenozoic	65,000,000	mammals, birds, bony fish
Mesozoic	225,000,000	primitive fish, amphibians, and reptiles
Palaeozoic	600,000,000	invertebrates, and primitive vertebrates
(Precambrian)	4,500,000,000	algae, bacteria, etc.

Palaeozoic, which opens some 600 million years ago with the Cambrian period. During the 375 million years of the Palaeozoic, primitive vertebrates evolved to such an extent that by Devonian times (middle Palaeozoic) certain types of fish had become land living Amphibia. By Permian times (end of the Palaeozoic), certain amphibians have evolved into primitive Reptilia. During the 160 million years of the Mesozoic, reptiles became the dominant form of life—the Age of the Dinosaurs was established. For some reason, the dinosaurs pass from the picture during the later Cretaceous. Early in the Mesozoic the Reptilia gave rise to two other Orders of vertebrates, the birds and the mammals. Neither, however, became common until after the demise of the dinosaurs. At the beginning of our present geologic era, the Cenozoic, birds and mammals began to replace the reptiles as the dominant forms of life. In good ethnocentric fashion, we usually refer to the Cenozoic as the Age of Mammals. But to maintain perspective, it should be remembered that birds and bony fish too are highly successful vertebrates during the Cenozoic. Also note that the invertebrates, especially the insects, are highly successful at the present time. This is the Age of Mammals only because we, as mammals, do the classifying.

Primates enter the fossil record during the Cretaceous (end of the Mesozoic). They become common during the Eocene (table 2.2), recede in Oligocene times, and show a fairly steady development since the Miocene, culminating in man during the Recent epoch.

Originally the geologic time scale could be tied to the Gregorian calendar only by educated guesses. However, as knowledge of the disintegration rate of various radioactive isotopes grew, it became possible to correlate the two scales. Although the correlation is still not perfect and many formations remain to be dated in absolute years, the scale of years given in table 1.1 can be considered correct as a first-order approximation. All these dates have some error, with the error larger for the earlier dates. But even if the date for the opening of the Palaeozoic is off by ten percent, the difference between 540 million and 600 million years is insignificant in our study.

VISUALIZING THE SPAN OF GEOLOGIC TIME

At the same time it must be recognized that a false impression could be gained from table 2.1 simply because we think of time more in terms of human generations rather than millions of years. It is like trying to comprehend the national debt when our usual use of money is in dollars and cents rather than the huge sums needed to run a country.

Consider that a dollar bill is about 4/1000th of an inch thick. If the thickness of a dollar bill represents one year, then the length of a football field is approximately one million years, and the time since the beginning of the Palaeozoic would be represented by 600 football fields. If the first creature who can be considered "man" appears 3 million years ago, then the last three football fields represent the age of man. But if we consider that written history began three thousand years ago, then history will be represented by less than the last foot of the last football field. It is apparent that on this time scale, the history of the United States would be a thickness less than the width of the final goal line. The moral of this analogy is that no table or chart can truly represent geologic time on a true scale. The later periods will always receive too much space. Another point is that when geologists speak of some event occurring rapidly, the absolute speed may be so slow as to be unmeasurable in terms of human generations.

But time is not the only difficult problem to visualize when considering the geologic past. Another is the positioning of the major land masses. Geologists have known for many years that the shape of the continents has changed somewhat and that mountain systems have come and gone. Not until the 1960s was it firmly established that continents have not always been in their present positions. In fact, it is now believed that some 200 million years ago (early in the Mesozoic) all continents were joined in one land mass known as Pangaea.[1] At some time during the start of the Cenozoic, South America became separate from Africa; later North America separated from Europe; and later still North and South America became joined. Without going into detail, this general picture should be kept in mind when the early history of the primates is considered.

The Cenozoic era is the time of the great development of the mammals and birds, although both groups had been in existence for a considerable period of time when the era opened. The primates developed during this era (see table 2.2). During the first epoch of the Quaternary—the Pleistocene—man makes his appearance. His history is intimately associated with the great climatic fluctuations of the Pleistocene (glacial age), and an approximation of the subdivisions of that epoch is shown in table 2.3.

TABLE 2.2. SUBDIVISIONS OF THE CENOZOIC ERA

Period	Epoch	Approximate number of years since beginning of epoch
Quaternary	Recent	10,000
	Pleistocene	3,000,000
Tertiary	Pliocene	12,000,000
	Miocene	25,000,000
	Oligocene	34,000,000
	Eocene	58,000,000
	Paleocene	65,000,000

The exact number of years given for the beginnings of these periods of geologic time are not too important. However, the reader should be conversant with the sequence of epochs for the Cenozoic and the subdivisions of the Pleistocene.

Much information concerning the process of phylogeny can be gained from a study of

1. J. T. Wilson, ed., *Continents Adrift: Readings from Scientific American.* (San Francisco: W. H. Freeman and Co., 1972).

TABLE 2.3. SUBDIVISIONS OF THE PLEISTOCENE EPOCH

Subdivision	European Glacier Names		Approximate number of years since beginning
Upper		Recent	10,000
	Würm		70,000
		Last Interglacial	100,000
Middle	Riss		200,000
		Great Interglacial	400,000
	Mindel		500,000
Lower		Interglacial II	
	Gunz		1,000,000
		Interglacial I	
	Donou		3,000,000

contemporary forms. But no extant form can be the ancestor of another. The course of phylogeny can be established only within the framework of geology and its subdiscipline palaeontology. To study change (and essentially phylogeny is change), time depth must be available. Only fossils in their geologic context can provide these necessary data.

SUMMARY

It is extremely difficult to think in terms of geologic time, as for most of us a human generation is a significant time period. From the point of view of geology, a hundred years is so short it cannot be measured. Table 2.1 places the beginning of the Cenozoic at 65 million years ago; if this dating is off by 5 million years, it would make no difference at all. In thinking of geologic time, try to assume that you are so rich you can lose $5 million and never know it. When you reach that point you will understand geologic time.

For Further Reading

Colbert, E. H. *Evolution of the Vertebrates: A History of the Backboned Animals Through Time.* New York: John Wiley & Sons, Science Editions, 1961.

Shelton, H. *Geology Illustrated.* San Francisco: W. H. Freeman and Company, 1966.

Bibliography

Wilson, J. T. ed., 1972. *Continents Adrift: Readings from Scientific American.* San Francisco: W. H. Freeman and Co.

3 The Genus *Homo* and Its Antecedents

Modern man belongs to the Genus *Homo* and to the single species *H. sapiens*. Although we tend to see a great deal of variation in contemporary *H. sapiens*, there is no difficulty, even morphologically, in distinguishing man from his pongid relatives. Man is the only erect, bipedal primate, and his skeleton reflects this locomotor adaptation. In any human population the cranial capacity will average at least 1,100 cc, although normal individual variability may range from 900 cc to 2,000 cc. The high skull has nearly vertical sides, a high forehead, and a well-rounded occiput. Brow ridges are either absent or minimally developed. The face is well under the cranium and is almost vertical. In some groups the region of the mouth may project a bit but never to the extent seen in pongids. There is a marked angle at the zygoma, a canine fossa just below the orbit, and a chin. The jaws are small, and the dental arch is evenly rounded. The canines do not project beyond the occlusal plane, and there is no diastema. The small size of the face, jaws, and teeth is paralleled by a small temporalis muscle attached to the side of the cranium and never reaching to the midsagittal plane. The occipital condyles are approximately in the center of the skull base, nearly evenly balancing the skull on the vertebral column.

Such a description of modern *H. sapiens* may be quite adequate in terms of skeletal morphology, but it omits an extremely important aspect of man's existence—culture. For contemporary man, culture is an all-pervasive force. It influences all aspects of his life, the way he looks at the world, and the way he exploits its resources. Man the biological animal and man the cultural animal are two aspects of human life so intimately intertwined that some recognize *H. sapiens* in the geologic record when there is evidence of culture, regardless of the associated morphology.[1] Because our main concern is with skeletal morphology, the development of man's culture during the past 3 million years must be omitted, but culture is undoubtedly the aspect of man which has made it possible for him to conquer and rule the world. To a large extent his morphology has been but a secondary reflection of this more important side of his success.

EARLY MAN

Just how long man has been on this earth depends on a definition of *Homo*. Most authorities recognize the Genus as being in existence for at least 500,000 years, but some

1. C. L. Brace, *The Stages of Human Evolution* (Englewood Cliffs, N. J.: Prentice-Hall, 1967).

put him back much further. Such disagreement among recognized authorities is understandable when you consider that phylogeny is a continuum through time. Therefore the time of a distinction between *Homo* and non-*Homo* must be an arbitrary one. People may use different criteria in establishing the boundary. This need not disturb us as we are more interested in the continuum than in the distinctions within it.

What is this continuum which leads from an ancestor shared by the pongids to man as we know him today? Working back in time we can trace modern man—*H. sapiens sapiens*—to the terminal portions of the Wurm glaciation. At that time man is well established over at least the continents of the Old World. He is an accomplished maker of stone tools (agriculture has not yet appeared); he controls fire; and he has a highly developed art. By implication he has a strong social organization undoubtedly based on the family, and has developed religion, with a concept of an afterlife.

Neanderthal Man

During the early part of the Wurm glaciation and the preceding interglacial period Europe, Africa, the Near East, and probably Asia were occupied by a form of man now called *H. sapiens neandertalensis*, or Neanderthal Man. Although placed in our Genus and species, Neanderthal Man is sufficiently different to warrant subspecific designation.

Though there is some disagreement with all typological designations, we may accept Aleš Hrdlička's definition of Neanderthal as the "Man of the Mousterian," a reference to the associated tool tradition. Certainly Neanderthal was an accomplished maker of flaked stone tools. He constructed shelters for himself in the caves of Europe, and because he buried his dead, we imply that he had rudimentary religious concepts.

Unfortunately the original description of Neanderthal depicted him as a round-shouldered, hairy caveman who could not walk completely upright. We now know that he was as good a biped as we, that he clothed himself (hence perhaps was not particularly hairy), and that, insofar as cranial capacity measures intelligence, he may well have had as much native intelligence as we.

At the same time he was morphologically different than modern man. Shorter than his successors, he was of muscular build. Even though his average cranial capacity was equivalent to ours, the vault of his skull was considerably lower, and he had a well-developed supraorbital torus (bar of bone extending across his forehead just above the orbits). His large face extended further forward beyond his cranium (facial prognathism) than ours, giving him a pseudobrutish appearance.

The original find of Neanderthal was made in Germany; most of the early discoveries were made in Germany, France, and Belgium. Most early archaeological work was done in that region, so such concentration is really not surprising. However, it has given us the impression that Neanderthal was a European man. But more recent finds show he was well represented in Africa (both north and south of the Sahara), in the Near East (Iran, Iraq, and Israel), southern Russia, and at least the island of Java in the Far East. With such a wide distribution, it is not surprising that there are identifiable regional differences both in the details of morphology and in the associated Mousterian tool tradition.

There has been considerable discussion concerning the exact role Neanderthal played in the ancestory of modern man. Did Neanderthal contribute genes to his successor *H. sapiens sapiens* or did the latter come into Europe suddenly and annihilate Neanderthal? Considering the now-known wide distribution of Neanderthal and the continuity in tool traditions, the former explanation is now more commonly held.[2]

Homo erectus

For approximately 700,000 years prior to Neanderthal, the Old World was occupied by a kind of man known today as *H. erectus*. Although not as well-known as Neanderthal, *H. erectus* remains have been found in Europe (although there is some question about these), Africa, China, and especially Java. *H. erectus* was a tool-using hominid who, at least in his later deposits, knew the use of fire. Skeletally, he is definitely more primitive than Neanderthal.

Although no pelvi have been found, *H. erectus* was an erect biped as the name implies. However, fossil bones of the postcranial skeleton and the position of the foramen magnum in the skull definitely indicate bipedalism, with arms freed from the chores of locomotion. On the other hand, the cranial capacity is less than modern—probably no more than 900 cc on the average. The skull vault is very low, and virtually no forehead existed because of the pronounced supraorbital torus. In addition to the supraorbital torus, other reinforcements of the skull are well-developed. The occipital torus, a ridge of bone extending across the back of the skull from one ear to the other, indicates a great development of the dorsal (back) neck muscles needed to offset the forward weight of the large face. Many specimens also show another ridge of bone extending along the midline of the skull vault. This bony development is probably due to the pull of large temporalis and masseter muscles, the two powerful muscles that close the jaws. In fact, all bones of the skull vault are quite thick; this, plus the robustness of the postcranial skeleton, indicates considerable muscular development throughout the body.

The face extended further beyond the cranium than did Neanderthal's. The teeth are not appreciably different from those of Neanderthal, but in some specimens the canine projects beyond the occlusal plane. Although some specimens also show a diastema, the anterior premolar is always a grinding tooth.

We may look on *H. erectus* as rather primitive, but remember he was successful for a long period of time, about three-quarters of the length of the last football field in our analogy. The tools he made were admittedly crude, but they must have been effective for there is evidence he routinely hunted large game. Further he is the earliest man to be found on the three continents of the Old World. His was no mean accomplishment.

Proceding back in time to the Lower Pleistocene we come to a stage of human ancestry which has generated considerable discussion. This is the time of the australopithecines found in southern and eastern Africa and probably also in Java. Strangely enough, the disagreements do not result from any dirth of fossil remains; quite the contrary, hominid fossils of this period are becoming common. Every year sees another half dozen or so added to the list. In fact, finds are being made so rapidly new remains are discovered before experts can write definitive reports on the previously discovered ones.

Important African Finds

Ever since Darwin, scientists have been looking for fossil evidence of the antecedents

2. D. S. Brose and W. H. Wolpoff, "Early Upper Paleolithic man and late Middle Paleolithic tools," *American Anthropologist* 73 (1971): 1156-1194; R. A. Dart, "*Australopithecus africanus:* the man-ape of South Africa," *Nature* 115 (1925): 195-99; J. Jelinek, "Neanderthal man and *Homo sapiens* in central and eastern Europe," *Current Anthropology* 10 (1969):475-92.

of man. The early Java discoveries of *H. erectus* focused attention on Asia as a likely place of human origins. Later discoveries made near Peking, China, of morphologically similar remains, had confirmed the opinion that Asia, not Africa, would yield material pertinent to the question. Therefore in 1925 when Raymond Dart published a short paper concerning a discovery in southern Africa, the scientific world was reluctant to accept his interpretation at face value. Since that time southern Africa, and later, under L. S. B. Leakey, eastern Africa have yielded a wealth of unexpectedly complex and significant material.

An initial problem hampering interpretation of the southern African material was the lack of an objective method for precisely dating the material. The geology of the region was practically unknown; there was no acceptable method of tying what was known of the geologic sequences into those already established in Europe. Furthermore, the geologic strata did not lend themselves to dating by radioactive isotopes. Although southern Africa has yielded a wealth of material, there is still no method for establishing beyond doubt the absolute dates of this material.[3] In the meantime Leakey had been working in eastern Africa, at Olduvai Gorge, Tanzania, and had located skeletal material in association with a geologic formation datable by the K/A (potassium-argon) technique. This yielded an age of 1.75 million years, a date far older than anyone had anticipated. This date seemed to establish that African material was older than that from Asia and therefore should antedate *Homo erectus*.

The Australopithecines

In 1925 Dart had given the name *Australopithecus africanus* to his original find; more material was discovered later, which on morphological grounds could be associated with this taxon. The total material indicated that a primate closely related to man lived in southern Africa at some early time but that certain morphological characteristics warranted a distinct taxonomic designation. This form, *A. africanus,* was small, probably no more than four feet tall and slightly built, weighing probably some 40 to 50 pounds. Cranial capacity ranged in the vicinity of 500 cc, within the range of extant pongids but definitely less than *H. erectus*. While the cranial vault was small, the face was relatively large, as was the mandible. The skull showed minimal marking for muscular attachment, and the reinforcement system—supraorbital and occipital tori and sagittal crest—showed minimal development. Associated postcranial bones confirmed the impression of a small, rather gracile group. The location of the foramen magnum and the form of the pelvic bones established that this was a bipedal animal. But whether *A. africanus* was as bipedally efficient as *H. erectus* is still an open question. The arcuate shape of the palate, the small canine teeth, the bicuspid form of the anterior, lower premolar clearly established that this form was more closely related to man than to any pongid. In fact, it might be thought that this taxon, *A. africanus*, could be a logical ancestor for *H. erectus*.

But the total southern African picture was not to be that simple. A few years after Dart's initial discovery, Robert Broom made a series of finds in much the same region. These indicated there were hominids in the region that did not fit the definition given by Dart; today these are usually referred to as *Australopithecus robustus.* This material indicated that these individuals probably stood about five feet tall and weighed about 100 pounds. As the name implies, they are

3. K. W. Butzer, "Paleoecology of South African Australopithecines: Taung revisited," *Current Anthropology* 15 (1974):367-382.

a more robust group than Dart's gracile species. Here the cranial capacity is about the same, but the skull shape is different. The supraorbital torus is more developed, the forehead is higher, there is a sagittal crest. The face is much wider but shows less prognathism. The jaw is massive with a high ascending ramus. If anything, the canines and incisors are smaller than those of *A. africanus,* but the postcanine teeth, the premolars and molars, are huge. Because of dating difficulties the relative ages of these two forms could not be precisely determined. It would have been nice to be able to show that the differences were due to sexual dimorphism, males larger than females, and that these were the two sexes of one species. It seemed strange, however, that the two forms were never found at the same site; a situation difficult to explain on the basis of sex. There was indirect evidence that the robust forms were probably more recent than the gracile.

When L. S. B. Leakey demonstrated that absolute dates could be obtained at Olduvai Gorge, many thought that by using these dates the southern African situation could be clarified. However, Olduvai Gorge added to the complexity. The gorge has five superimposed beds, but the material pertinent to the australopithecine controversy comes from Beds I and II; K/A dates indicate that Bed I probably extends back to about 2 million years B.P. (before present) and lasts about a million years.

It was in the lower part of Bed I that Leakey discovered remains that he called "*Zinjanthropus*" *boisei.* Today, most authorities place this in the genus *Australopithecus* and either in the species *A. robustus* or retain Leakey's original specific designation but recognize that it has close affinity to the robust form of southern Africa. Work in southern Africa had led investigators to expect the gracile form in earlier deposits; yet here was the earliest dated remains, and they were definitely of robust morphology. To further complicate matters, Bed I had cultural remains; at that time such remains were unknown in the south.

As work progressed at Olduvai, it became apparent that the robust form was not alone in Bed I; a gracile form was also present. Leakey originally established a new taxon, *Homo habilis,* for these gracile remains; today some investigators retain this name but others would assign these also to *Australopithecus.* At least here was a site where both a robust and gracile form were found together. But the question remains, are they different at the species or at the generic level, or is this simply sexual dimorphism with one species?[4] The question is unresolved; work is continuing but it would appear that additional material, although welcome, will not resolve the question. Better methods of analyzing material already available would seem to offer more hope for a solution.[5]

In the meantime, Richard Leakey, a son of L. S. B. Leakey, along with French and American colleagues, had begun work east of Lake Rudolf in Kenya and along the Omo River in southern Ethiopia. Like Olduvai, this region was subjected to volcanic activity, and therefore K/A can be used to give absolute dates. The region is particularly rich in hominid remains with additional finds being reported annually. The later finds overlap Bed I, Olduvai, but the earlier deposits carry the story back to at least 4 million years B.P. One find of a tooth from the Baringo Basin, Kenya, may carry the australopithecine story back to 9 million years.

4. R. S. Corruccini, "Multivariate analysis of *Gigantopithecus* mandibles," *American Journal of Physical Anthropology* 42 (1975):167-170.

5. D. W. Read, "Hominid teeth and their relationship to hominid phylogeny," *American Journal of Physical Anthropology* 42 (1975):105-126.

Originally there was the feeling that probably the australopithecine stage represented a transitional form between man's common ancestor with the apes and the direct line leading to modern man. There was a disagreement concerning the number of species and/or Genera involved. Even Dart referred to his find as an "ape-man," thereby implying a transitional type. From some segment of this diverse population must have come the ancestors of *H. erectus*. The more recent finds and better dating techniques have changed this view. If the australopithecines of northern Kenya extend back only 4 million years and the latest of them, which may well be Dart's original find is less than a million years old, then this is no transitional form.[6] The australopithecines had a long, honorable history in Africa and perhaps Asia as well. They must be looked upon as a successful taxon.

MAN'S EARLIEST ANCESTOR?

Two events occurred in the early 1970s which have raised questions as to whether or not the australopithecines can be considered as ancestor to *H. erectus*. The first of these was the discovery in 1972 by Richard Leakey of a skull known as ER 1470.[7] The find was made in the East Rudolf area and has been dated at 2.8 million years. The skull is that of a gracile individual who lacks the reinforcement system of the skull seen in the robust forms. It is said that the teeth differ significantly from those of the australopithecines and, most importantly, the cranial capacity has been estimated at 800 cc, a value virtually within the range of *H. erectus*. Leakey feels this is an example of *Homo habilis*, and that the Genus *Homo* must extend back to the early days of the australopithecines. Certainly if the initial, brief description of this find and its dating withstand detailed analysis, then *Homo* would be older than any of the southern African material, and hence none of those forms could have contributed to the subsequent *Homo erectus*.

The second event of the 1970s was the continued discovery of hominid remains in Java and China, and a potentially older reckoning of *H. erectus* through the application of more sophisticated dating methods. In fact, Sartono would date some at approximately 2 million years B.P.[8] If this is the case, then *H. erectus* was an Asian contemporary of some of the African australopithecines.

Just how this wealth of material will eventually be interpreted isn't clear; however, man's ancestry can now be traced back to at least the late Pliocene. By the early Pleistocene he is to be found in both Asia and Africa. More material concerning the events of this time is becoming available, but the riddle will not be resolved until modern dating techniques and more sophisticated analytical techniques are used or developed for interpretation.

The most likely candidate for man's earlier ancestry would appear to be *Ramapithecus*. This Genus, known from both India and Africa, has dates ranging from 18 million years in eastern Africa to the latest at about 9 million years in India. This Genus is represented by parts of the face and upper jaw, teeth, and parts of the mandible. These indicate an animal with a hominid-shaped palate, short face, and small canines and incisors. The molars show a thickening of the enamel and this plus the abrasions on the crowns and the small canines lead to the conclusion that this animal chewed its food

6. Butzer, *Paleoecology*, pp. 367-82.

7. R. E. Leakey, "Skull 1470," *National Geographic Magazine* 143 (1973):819-829.

8. S. Sartono, "Implications arising from *Pithecanthropus* VIII," IXth International Congress of Anthropological and Ethnological Sciences (Chicago: 1973).

in a rotary fashion, as in modern man. This is the kind of morphology one would expect to precede either *H. habilis,* an australopithecine, or a *H. erectus.* Apparently *Ramapithecus* was not a common Genus but may well have been semiterrestrial. Perhaps he was relegated to this ecological niche because of competition with the dryopithecines. It is within this latter group that we expect to find the common ancestor of man and his ape cousins. They will be discussed as we review the history of the Pongidae.

SUMMARY

Man, *Homo sapiens sapiens,* can be traced back to the terminal phases of the Wurm glaciation. At that time he has already developed a complex culture based on hunting and gathering rather than on agriculture. Prior to this time another subspecies, *H. sapiens neandertalensis,* is known from Europe, Asia, and Africa. Although morphologically different from modern man, these people were as much erect bipeds as we; their cranial capacity was equal to ours, but they were more muscular and identifiably different.

During the middle Pleistocene, Asia, Africa, and probably Europe were the home of *Homo erectus.* These people, with a crude stone tool tradition, had a cranial capacity definitely smaller than our own, were most brutish in appearance, but were bipedal in their mode of locomotion.

Just when *H. erectus* differentiated from his predecessor isn't known. It had been thought that the australopithecines of southern and eastern Africa and probably of Asia were his antecedents. The situation is now known to be far more complicated. There may be at least two species of *Australopithecus;* the Genus *Homo* may be older than most of the finds reported to date, and, to make the matter more complicated, *H. erectus,* himself, may be as old as any of them. Not just more material is needed to solve this problem; we also need more efficient methods of analysis to unravel the strands of this puzzle.

Classification of taxa used in chapter 3:

- Order: Primates
  - Suborder: Anthropoidea
    - Infraorder: Catarrhini
      - Superfamily: Hominoidea
        - Family: Hominidae
          - Genus: *Homo*
            - Species: *H. sapiens* — Upper Pleitocene-Recent (man)
              H. erectus — Middle Pleistocene
          - Genera: *Australopithecus*—Early Pleistocene
            Ramapithecus—Miocene-Pliocene

For Further Reading

Clark, W. E. L. *The Fossil Evidence for Human Evolution,* rev. ed. Chicago: University of Chicago Press, 1964. A summary of the evidence for human evolution by one of the outstanding authorities on the subject.

———. *Man-Apes or Ape-Men? The Story of Discoveries in Africa.* New York: Holt, Rinehart, and Winston, 1967. A history of the events following Dart's original announcement of fossil man in Africa.

Leakey, L. S. B., J. Prost, and S. Prost, eds. *Adam or Ape: A Sourcebook of Discoveries About Early Man.* Cambridge, Mass.: Schenkman Publishing Co., 1971. A reprinting of many of the important, original papers dealing with human evolution.

Bibliography

Brace, C. L. 1967. *The Stages of Human Evolution.* Englewood Cliffs, N. J.: Prentice-Hall.

Brose, D. S. and W. H. Wolpoff. 1971. "Early Upper Paleolithic man and late Middle

Paleolithic tools." *American Anthropologist* 73:1156-1194.

Butzer, K. W. 1974. "Paleoecology of South African Australopithecines: Taung revisited." *Current Anthropology* 15:367-382.

Corruccini, R. S. 1975. "Multivariate analysis of *Gigantopithecus* mandibles." *American Journal of Physical Anthropology* 42:167-170.

Dart, R. A. 1925. "*Australopithecus africanus:* the man-ape of South Africa." *Nature* 115: 195-99.

Jelinek, J. 1969. "Neanderthal man and *Homo sapiens* in central and eastern Europe." *Current Anthropology* 10:475-92.

Leakey, R. E. 1973. "Skull 1470." *National Geographic Magazine* 143:819-829.

Read, D. W. 1975. "Hominid teeth and their relationship to hominid phylogeny." *American Journal of Physical Anthropolgy* 42: 105-126.

Sartono, S. 1973. "Implications arising from *Pithecanthropus* VIII." IXth International Congress of Anthropological and Ethnological Sciences, Chicago: Ill.

4 The Pongidae and the Hylobatidae

Scientists presently disagree over the classification of the apes. This disagreement centers around two points. First, should the chimpanzee and gorilla be in separate Genera or in only one? Traditional use of morphology had placed them in separate Genera, *Pan* for the chimpanzee and *Gorilla* for the gorilla. Recent work in comparative biochemistry, immunology, and karyotypology (see Glossary) indicates that these two should be included in but one Genera—*Pan,* according to the rules of nomenclature. We will accept the second point of view for purposes of this discussion.

The second area of disagreement revolves around the classification of the gibbon and siamang. These are placed in separate Genera, *Hylobates* and *Symphalangus* respectively. But the question has been raised whether these two should constitute the Subfamily Hylobatinae, with the other apes in the Ponginae (both in the Family Pongidae), or whether the gibbon and siamang should be placed in a separate Family Hylobatidae. These, the smallest of the apes, do differ morphologically from the others in a monkeylike direction. For example, they have ischial collosities not found in the other apes but found in monkeys, and the cusp pattern of their molars also show monkeylike affinities. Biochemically and immunologically, they would be the most deviant of the Pongidae if included in that Family. For purposes of our discussion it will be convenient to recognize two Families, the Hylobatidae and the Pongidae. The antecedents of these will be discussed separately.

PONGID ANTECEDENTS

Within the Family Pongidae we recognize two contemporary Genera, *Pan* (including the chimpanzee and gorilla of Africa) and *Pongo,* the orangutan of Sumatra and Borneo. These two would be combined in the Subfamily Ponginae. Whether viewed morphologically, physiologically, or biochemically, the Genus *Pan* is closer to *Homo* than is *Pongo,* but none of the Ponginae is well represented in the fossil record. In fact, there is no fossil universally accepted as ancestral to the orangutan.

For the Genus *Pan* the situation is different, although even here the picture is not complete. During the Pleistocene, no evident direct ancestor for this Genus has been found. However, a rather aberrant, probably unrelated form is known from the Lower Pleistocene (in southern China); it extends back to at least the middle Pliocene (in northern India). This creature, *Gigantopithecus,* may well have been the largest primate ever evolved. Its exact size is a question as the remains consist solely of teeth and mandibles, but if these parts were in the same proportion to total body size as in the gorilla, *Gigantopithecus* would have been the larger animal.

From Pliocene into Lower Pleistocene times, the forests were dwindling and probably *Gigantopithecus* was adapting to open-country living. This would imply a shift to more abrasive foods; and the morphology of the teeth and mandibles is in line with this assumption. The incisors are rather small and set vertically in the bone. The anterior premolars were losing their function of honing against the upper canines; the lower canines, though still large, were worn down rapidly, probably indicating a rotary motion during chewing. The molars were high-crowned and very large. The mandible was deep and robust. This pattern indicates a vegetarian primate living in fairly open country and eating foods that would rapidly wear the teeth. The morphology differs enough from that of *Pan* to rule out *Gigantopithecus* as a direct ancestor. Some have seen a resemblance to *Australopithecus*, but time precludes *Gigantopithecus* as a likely ancestor. Similarities are more likely due to adaptations to similar environmental conditions.

Dryopithecine Characteristics

The Miocene and the early Pliocene saw a widespread group of primates who are likely candidates as ancestors of the later pongids. Originally given many generic names, all are now included in the Subfamily Dryopithecinae (Family Pongidae), and those from this time period are placed in the Genus *Dryopithecus*. This Genus has now been identified from Europe, eastward through the southern Soviet Union, the Middle East, China, India, and more recently in eastern Africa. The species of *Dryopithecus* range in size from one about the size of contemporary gibbons to that of the gorilla. In terms of geographic distribution and species differentiation, this is the most successful Genera of the Pongidae. The species from eastern Africa are probably the older while those from Eurasia may well have lasted to somewhat more recent times.

Although known mainly from teeth and mandibles, the Genus is also represented by an almost complete skull and a number of postcranial bones. But complete skeletons must be uncovered before the behavioral patterns of this important taxon can be better understood. However, *Dryopithecus* was undoubtedly a forest living ape because its remains are always associated with a forest fauna. In addition, detailed examination of the postcranial skeletal remains indicates a quadrupedal mode of locomotion. Thus it seems likely that these animals did not exploit the forests in the same manner as contemporary *Pan;* that is, these animals were not adapted to a brachiating mode of locomotion.

In the facial region, the anterior muzzle of *Dryopithecus* is much narrower than is that of *Pan*. This narrowing is associated with the small, closely set incisors. In *Pan* these teeth have become spatulate and are procumbent; in the jaw of *Dryopithecus* they are set vertically.

In 1933, Hopwood found the remains of a dryopithecine in Miocene deposits of Kenya. Hopwood felt that he had discovered the ancestor of the modern chimpanzee. He established the Genus *"Proconsul"* for his eastern African form, which he named after a chimpanzee called Consul in the London Zoo. Since then much additional material has become available, and investigators now consider these remains *Dryopithecus africanus*. This is one of the smaller dryopithecines, about the size of the pygmy chimpanzee, *Pan paniscus*. Many features of the postcranial skeleton suggest *D. africanus* was adopting an arm swinging mode of locomotion, although these changes had not progressed to the typical proportion seen in modern brachiators. The skull lacked the heavy bony reinforcement typical of *Pan*, such as heavy brow ridges, nuchal torus, large face, and the bony reinforcement across the inner aspect of the anterior part of the mandible, the so-called simian shelf. In fact, *D. africanus* was a much more glacile animal than is *Pan*. For all of that, detailed studies of teeth, wrist, and foot indicate that this is the Miocene ancestor of the chimpanzee.

Some early investigators had felt that *D. africanus* might be the common ancestor of man and chimpanzee, but this now seems unlikely. *Ramapithecus* appears to be a more likely candidate for man's Miocene ancestor for a number of reasons. One is that it lacks the enlarged canine and associated sectorially shaped lower anterior premolar of the dryopithecines. Another reason is that the arcuate shape of the *Ramapithecus* palate anticipates the condition found in man whereas that of *D. africanus* is more like that of modern apes, U-shaped.

Whereas *D. africanus* was a small form, *D. indicus* was about the size of a gorilla. Although rather widespread in Asia during the Miocene, the center of the *D. indicus* distribution seems to have been northern India. Examination of the teeth and facial structure indicates that this form is a more likely ancestor for *Gigantopithecus* than for the gorilla.

In recent years remains of the face, mandible, and teeth of a large dryopithecine have been found in Miocene deposits of Uganda and Kenya. These are now classified in the species *D. major*. Detailed studies of the mandibles, palate, and particularly the teeth indicate a close relation to *P. gorilla*. Unfortunately, with the possible exception of a talus (a tarsal bone of the foot), postcranial remains are unknown. These remains do seem to indicate that the chimpanzee and gorilla are closely related but that they have been separated, at the species level, since Miocene times. In any event, their development seems to have been restricted to Africa.

The dryopithecines evidently were successful, widespread pongids during the Miocene-Pliocene times. They were forest-living but had not developed all the specializations seen in their modern descendants. The number of species (seven or more) and their wide distribution indicates not only that they were more successful than contemporary pongids but also that man cannot be the sole blame for the comparative lack of success of our modern cousins. In fact, but for enlightened, modern conservation measures, our pongid relatives might now be extinct.

PONGID BEGINNINGS

As the Miocene represents the heyday of the Pongidae, the Oligocene should be the period for that Family's establishment. Unfortunately the Oligocene, and especially its final third, is not well represented in the geologic record. For primate paleontology, it is a very underrepresented period. The only primate fossils from the Oligocene are found in the Fayum region of Egypt, and all these date from its early portion. Just how representative the Fayum population may be is of course unknown, but the region has yielded some interesting specimens for our understanding of the early Dryopithecinae.

During the early Oligocene, the Fayum, now a desert, was a well-watered, thickly forested area, the ideal environment for the prosperity of early anthropoids. Simultaneously, it was a poor environment for the fossilization of arboreal animals. Though some finds were made in the early part of this century, the Yale Expedition later discovered its real potentialities.[1]

1. For a popular account of this work see E. L. Simons, "The earliest apes," *Scientific American* 317 (1967):28-35.

Three Genera of Dryopithecinae are recognized from the early Oligocene of the Fayum. *Aegyptopithecus* was originally established from a portion of a mandible, but since that time several other mandibles, an almost complete skull, and an ulna have been found. The morphology of these remains indicates that *Aegyptopithecus* was a small, agile, arboreal pongid who probably lived on leaves and fruits. This is the morphology to be expected for an ancestor not only of *Dryopithecus* but also for *Ramapithecus*. Thus it seems likely that *Aegyptopithecus* was a common ancestor for both *Pan* and *Homo*.

The incisors are small and the anterior portion of the snout is narrow; the tooth rows diverge posteriorly. The canines are large, and the lower anterior premolar honed against the upper canine. The upper premolars are bicuspids. The detailed morphology of the molars resembles the later dryopithecines. The skull shows a marked postorbital constriction. The cranial vault is small relative to the size of the face, and, as would be expected under these circumstances, there are both sagittal and nuchal crests. Large molars plus the implied large chewing muscles probably indicate a herbivorous diet.

As in all Anthropoidea there is a bony plate separating the orbital from the temporal fossae. However, the tympanic ring does not extend into the external auditory meatus, indicating that this modern criterion of the Anthropoidea had not yet developed.

Another of the early Oligocene Genera was *Propliopithecus*. Found in the early part of this century its exact geologic context is not known, but it is probably somewhat earlier than *Aegyptopithecus*. *Propliopithecus* remains consist of the two horizontal rami of a mandible with complete dentition except for the incisors and left canine. The sockets for these teeth are present so their orientation and general size can be determined. The canines are small, and although the anterior premolar has but a single cusp it does not have the compressed anterior border which would be expected if this tooth honed against the upper canine as in later pongids. Originally, *Propliopithecus* was placed in the Hylobatidae, but recent comparisons with newly available material indicate it should be included in the Pongidae.

The third recognized pongid Genus from the Oligocene is *Oligopithecus*. The findings, a small mandible, are those of the oldest primate in the Fayum region. The canine is small and the anterior premolar has the bladelike edge, showing that it honed against a sharp upper canine. Although the cusp pattern of the molars justifies the inclusion of this Genus in the dryopithecines, there are resemblances to earlier prosimians to be discussed later.

One feature characteristic of man and his modern, near relatives is not only the absolute and relative increase in brain size but also the unique complexity of the brain. Among fossils, especially when bones of the cranial vault are seldom preserved, changes in brain morphology are difficult to document. Fortunately, *Aegyptopithecus* and some of the dryopithecines are represented by sufficiently complete crania to warrant some statements about brain development. Evidence indicates that by the time of *Aegyptopithecus*, some 27 million to 30 million years ago, the brain was definitely advanced over the prosimian condition. The visual cortex is expanded while the olfactory bulbs and associated structures are reduced. Sulci of the brain are apparent and separate the primary somatic sensory from the motor cortex. Thus by early Oligocene times the anthropoid brain is well on its way toward its modern condition.[2]

2. L. Radinsky, "The fossil evidence of anthropoid brain evolution," *American Journal of Physical Anthropology* 41 (1974):15-27.

Although the fossil history of the Family Pongidae is far from complete, the pongids were well established by Oligocene times. Just how widespread it was cannot be determined from presently available data. A successful group of primates, the Family was distributed widely over the three continents of the Old World by Miocene times. Following the Miocene there seems to have been a decline which culminates in the restricted, noncontiguous distribution seen today. Although the forest homes of the Pongidae became restricted, part of their decline may also be due to the rise of the monkeys during later Miocene and Pliocene times. The recent spread of *Homo,* especially since the development of agriculture, has certainly not helped *Pan* and *Pongo* escape probable extinction.

HYLOBATIDAE—THE LESSER APES

Man and the Family Pongidae are included in the Superfamily Hominoidea. Also included in that Superfamily is the Family Hylobatidae—the lesser apes, so-called because of their smaller body size. Today the Hylobatidae are represented by *Hylobates* (the gibbon) and by *Symphalangus* (the siamang). These two Genera are very similar except that the latter is about twice the size of the former. Interestingly enough, *Symphalangus* has 50 chromosomes (per body cell) whereas *Hylobates* has only 44. These and other data indicate that they are distinct genera.

The lesser apes are presently restricted to southeast Asia, but they have a wider distribution than *Pongo.* In terms of number of animals and, for *Hylobates,* number of species, these seem to be more successful than either *Pan* or *Pongo;* they, and especially *Hylobates,* are not in as great a danger of extinction as their larger cousins.

Fossil remains show that the ancestors of contemporary primates tended to be small animals, and perhaps for that reason many fossil forms were considered at first to be ancestoral to the gibbon. But more recent data have suggested differently.

The contemporary Hylobatidae are the acrobats of the jungle having developed very long upper extremities for brachiation. Though brachiation is also used by the Pongidae, their larger body size prevents great agility in the trees. Some New World monkeys, especially *Ateles* (the spider monkey) are also brachiators, but they usually have prehensile tails, which they use as a fifth appendage. No Old World primate has a prehensile tail; in fact, the Hominoidea have lost their tails entirely.

In the fossil record *Symphalangus* and *Hylobates* are both known from Pleistocene deposits in Java while the latter species is also found at the same time in China. Today, only *Hylobates* is found in Java, and neither is in China. Their present distribution is somewhat restricted probably because of the rise of the monkeys.

Gibbons and siamangs are usually placed in the Subfamily Hylobatinae, unknown prior to the Pleistocene. Forms ancestoral to the Hylobatinae are grouped in the Subfamily Pliopithecinae, which may have extended into the Pliocene but is much better represented in the Miocene and Oligocene. There are two Miocene genera, *Pliopithecus* and *Limnopithecus.*

Pliopithecus is known mainly from Europe, but its range may have extended to northern Africa and Asia. A number of species are recognized based mainly on jaws and teeth. However, almost the entire skeleton is known for the genus as a whole. The remains indicate that *Pliopithecus* was a small, arboreal primate who had not developed the specializations for brachiation seen in Hylobatinae. The postcranial skeleton shows some modifications in that direction, but most features are those to be expected at a generalized hominoid level.

Study of the sacrum indicates that a tail was present. The long bones indicate that the extremities were of approximately the same length; the humerus is straight-shafted like that of the Hylobatinae but unlike that of the Dryopithecinae. Interestingly enough, in some the humerus has an entepicondylar foramen. This foramen, located at the medial condyle of the humerus, is found in New World monkeys but is very rare in present-day hominoids. The lower extremity also shows resemblances to both the Hylobatinae and some of the larger New World monkeys but differs from Miocene Dryopithecinae.

The general structure of the cranium and face is gibbonlike although like other Miocene hominoids, the anterior portion of the muzzle is narrow, and the tooth rows diverge posteriorly. The daggerlike canine teeth resemble those of gibbons with the upper honing against the lower, anterior premolar. The posterior premolar is bicuspid as in gibbons. The lower molars have the typical five-cusp pattern of hominoids, but the uppers are relatively broader than extant forms.

Pliopithecus could make a good ancestor for the Hylobatinae. If so, its geographical distribution would indicate that the gibbon evolved outside of Asia and migrated there during Pliocene times.

The other Miocene Genus is *Limnopithecus,* found exclusively in eastern Africa. Originally based on two mandibular fragments found in 1933, the Genus is now known from specimens representing almost the entire skeleton. Unfortunately, no complete skull has been found. Although older than *Pliopithecus,* this Genus also shows resemblances to the Hylobatinae. The long bones of the extremities indicate a shift in the direction of brachiation; the one humerus found lacks the entepicondylar foramen of *Pliopithecus.* Again the morphology of the postcranial skeleton shows resemblances to both the Hylobatinae and to the larger New World monkeys. In the facial region *Limnopithecus* resembles *Pliopithecus,* the difference being a shorter, broader snout and a deeper, more robust mandible. *Limnopithecus* could be ancestoral either to *Pliopithecus* or directly to the Hylobatinae.

An interesting Genus, *Acolopithecus,* has been found in Oligocene deposits from the Fayum. As mentioned previously, the Fayum today is a desert and is subject to very strong winds. One morning members of the Yale Expedition discovered a mandible being uncovered by heavy winds. Its morphology justified the establishment of a new Genus so it was named for Aeolus, the Greek god of the winds.

The mandible is complete except for the ascending rami and the incisor teeth. It is only about half the size of *Aegyptopithecus,* but it contains relatively large canines with very thick roots. The incisor sockets indicate that these teeth were probably large and procumbent, a condition also found in *Limnopithecus.* Procumbent incisors are found in Ponginae but not in Hylobatinae. The anterior premolar is sectorial, honed against the upper canine, and the third molar is small compared to the other two.

The exact affiliations of *Aeolopithecus* are not known, but they would appear to be with the Pliopithecinae. This does not necessarily mean that *Aeolopithecus* is a direct ancestor of *Pliopithecus.*

In this discussion we have included three Families, Hylobatidae, Pongidae, and Hominidae, in the Superfamily Hominoidea. This implies that the common ancestor for these three Families was more recent than the common ancestor of any one of these Families and that of any other primate. This view is predicated on the older ideas based mainly on comparative morphology and an admittedly incomplete fossil record. Because of karyotypological and some biochemical similarities between the Hylobatidae and other primates, some authorities have questioned the placement of Hylobatidae in the Hominoidea. They would prefer its placement with the Old World monkeys. Until a more complete fossil record is available, there appears to be no present advantage in shifting this group's taxonomic placement. But regardless of how this minor point is resolved the important thing is that in many respects the Hylobatidae and especially its Subfamily Hylobatinae are transitional between the Pongidae and Hominidae and the other Anthropoidea. The major point is that all life implicitly represents a continuum in time but the establishment of biological classification schemes arbitrarily break up that continuum. Therefore no classification of life forms can ever be perfect in an absolute sense.

Before leaving the Hominoidea, we must say a few words about two additional Genera, *Amphipithecus* and *Pondaungia.* These come from upper Eocene deposits of Burma. Because both are incomplete specimens and are very early in primate history, their exact affiliations are uncertain. *Amphipithecus* consists of a portion of a mandible that probably held three premolars. All modern members of the Infraorder Catarrhini have only two premolars, but since primitive mammals had three premolars we would expect a catarrhine ancestor to have that many. The mandible is very deep, a feature usually associated with the anterior fusion of the two mandibular halves; that is, this form may have had a fused mandibular symphysis. If so, the remains are of a catarrhine. The molar morphology seems to be close to that of later Hominoidea.

The other Genus, *Pondaungia,* consists of a partial left maxilla and the horizontal rami of a mandible. Because of the circumstances of the find, these may represent one individual. The general morphology of this find and especially the cusp arrangement on the upper molars seem to anticipate the condition found in the Hominoidea.

In attempting to interpret these forms a number of points must be kept in mind. They occurred geologically early in primate history, a time when the primates were not highly differentiated from other early mammals and when primates show considerable variability. As will be discussed later, this is a condition to be expected in the early differentiation of an Order. Under such conditions it is extremely difficult to classify imperfectly known forms. Thus perhaps these are not primates at all, but this seems unlikely. Another possibility is that although they belong to the Order Primates, they may not be ancestoral to any modern taxon. A more likely possibility is that they are close to the early differentiation of Hominoidea, but if this is the case the Hominoidea would be older than the Cercopithecoidea (to be discussed in the next chapter). If true, then either the monkeys evolved from the ape stem (a conclusion opposite to the traditional picture), or the monkey and ape line evolved independently from prosimian ancestors. If the latter is so, then there is no justification for the Infraorder Catarrhini. This taxonomic nicety will be reconsidered after we discuss the Cercopithecoidea.

SUMMARY

Man's closest contemporary taxonomic relatives are found among the Pongidae, represented today by *Pan* (chimpanzee and gorilla) and *Pongo* (orangutan). Limited geographic distribution and the small number of extant species make this Family a fairly unsuccessful group. Though man's recent agricultural intrusion into their surroundings has added to their present problems, the wide distribution and extent of forebearer species in the Miocene suggest some additional factor must have contributed to their decline.

The Pongidae are not well represented in the Pleistocene and Pliocene fossil record, but are well-known during the Miocene. Ancestoral Genera are known from the Oligocene, even though fossil-primate-bearing strata are very scarce during that epoch. During the Oligocene one Genus, *Aegyptopithecus,* could be a common but not necessarily the most recent ancestor of both Pongidae and Hominidae. It is possible that these two lines did not separate until much later.

A phyletic line can also be established for the Hylobatidae tracing their ancestry back to the Oligocene. There is a question as to whether the Hylobatidae should be included in the Anthropoidea or be transferred to the Cercopithecoidea. Assuming its present taxonomic position is correct, the common anthropoid ancestor may be represented in the Eocene. However, the two Genera from that epoch are not well-known, not only because of a paucity of specimens but also because the identifiable criteria seen in modern forms had not yet evolved in the early ones. If further research indicates that *Amphipithecus* and *Pondaungia* are truly anthropoids, then Anthropoidea must have differentiated prior to the Cercopithecoidea. Classification of forms discussed in chapter 4:

- Order: Primates
  - Suborder: Anthropoidea
    - Infraorder: Catarrhini
      - Superfamily: Hominoidea
        - Family: Pongidae
          - Subfamily: Ponginae
            - Genera: *Pan*—Recent (chimpanzee and gorilla)
              Pongo—Recent (orangutan)
          - Subfamily: Gigantopithecinae
            - Genus: *Gigantopithecus*—Pliocene-Pleistocene
          - Subfamily: Dryopithecinae
            - Genera: *Dryopithecus*—Miocene-Pliocene
              Aegyptopithecus—Oligocene
              Propliopithecus—Oligocene
              Oligopithecus—Oligocene
        - Family: Hylobatidae
          - Subfamily: Hylobatinae
            - Genera: *Hylobates*—Pleistocene-Recent (gibbon)
              Symphalangus—Pleistocene-Recent (siamang)
          - Subfamily: Pliopithecinae
            - Genera: *Pliopithecus*—Miocene-Pliocene
              Limnopithecus—Miocene
              Aeolopithecus—Oligocene
      - Superfamily: Homonoidea?
        - Genera: *Amphipithecus*—Eocene
          Pondaungia—Eocene

For Further Reading

Clark, W. E. L. *The Antecedents of Man: An Introduction to the Evolution of the Primates.* Chicago: Quadrangle Books, 1960. This is a very good review of the fossil evidence known at the time of publication. Emphasis is placed on the implications of comparative primate anatomy.

Simons, E. L. *Primate Evolution: An Introduction to Man's Place in Nature.* The Macmillan Series in Physical Anthropology. New York: Macmillan Co., 1972. Contains more up-to-date information on the fossil record than does Clark but has less information on comparative primate anatomy.

Bibliography

Radinsky, L. 1974. "The fossil evidence of anthropoid brain evolution." *American Journal of Physical Anthropology* 41:15-27.

Simons, E. L. 1967. "The earliest apes." *Scientific American* 317:28-35.

5 The Cercopithecoidea and Oreopithecoidea

Having completed our discussions of the Hominoidea, we have two Superfamilies remaining in the Infraorder Catarrhini, the Cercopithecoidea and Oreopithecoidea. The latter is extinct, however.

Today the Cercopithecoidea are common, diurnal primates in Africa south of the Sahara and in India. They are also found on the islands of Indonesia, the Philippines, and on the northern Japanese islands and a small area of the adjacent mainland. Interestingly enough, they are also represented on the Rock of Gibraltar (the only nonhuman primate found in Europe) and a small area just south of the Rock in northern Africa.

Cercopithecidae is the sole Family recognized, but it is divided into three Subfamilies, Cercopithecinae, Colobinae, and the extinct Parapithecinae. The first Subfamily has as many as eight extant Genera with probably 45 species. The Colobinae has seven living Genera with 33 species. Obviously, such diversity cannot be discussed in detail here, especially if the extinct Genera are included. Considering the number of species (78 or more depending on the authority consulted) and the great geographical range (all three continents of the Old World), it must be apparent that these monkeys have adapted to a wide range of ecological niches. They range from highly arboreal species who seldom descend from the trees to savannah-adapted forms who seldom invade the trees. Some are found in thickly forested, swampy regions while others live in dry, rocky areas almost devoid of trees. The group is so variably adapted that even their skeletal morphology reflects this variability; hence the description given below is necessarily an overgeneralization.

TRAITS OF THE OLD WORLD MONKEYS

Like all Catarrhini, the dental formula of the Cercopithecoidea is $2.1.2.3/2.1.2.3 = 32$ and, like many of the Hominoidea, the anterior lower premolar has a compressed anterior border that shears against the upper canine. Unlike the Hominoidea, the canine is usually a saberlike tooth, long in relation to its cross section. Probably the most diagnostic dental feature, at least for the extant forms, is the bilophodont molar cusp pattern (see fig. 1.2).

In body size these animals range from the small talapoin monkey, where males weigh slightly more than one kilogram, the females just under one kilogram, to some of the baboons where the males may weigh 30 kilograms and the females about half as much. All species are basically quadrupedal and plantigrade; that is, they walk on all four extremities, even in the trees, and place the hands and feet flat on the ground. In the more terrestrial forms the heel of the palm may be raised with the animal carrying his weight on the flexor side of the fingers. This modification lengthens the upper extremities and permits faster running.

Associated with a quadrupedal mode of locomotion, the chest is narrower than deep, and the lumbar region of the spine is longer than the thoracic region. The iliac portion of the *os coxae* (hipbone) is a narrow blade which extends cranially parallel to the vertebral column.

Most species show sexual dimorphism, with males being larger than females. The generally larger semiterrestrial species display this more than the strictly arboreal forms.

There is a moderate degree of facial prognathism; that is, the face extends anterior to the brain. In baboons this feature has been accentuated to produce a long, doglike muzzle. All species have ischial collosities, a thickened layer of skin overlying the enlarged ischial tuberosities of the *os coxae*. These have been viewed as sitting adaptations.

The thumb and great toe are both opposable, but the thumb does not show a human degree of opposability and thus lacks the human precision grip. All digits of course are equipped with flat nails. The tail is of variable length—being short or almost absent in the semiterrestrial forms but equal to or greater than body length in the more arboreal ones.

The Family Cercopithecidae is represented today by two Subfamilies, Cercopithecinae in Africa and Colobinae in Asia. However, neither Subfamily is restricted to one continent. The Cercopithecinae has one Genus, *Macaca*, that is found primarily in Asia. Most living species of this Genus (most authorities recognize about twelve) are found in India and southeast Asia; one is found in northern Japan and adjacent parts of China; and one is located in southern Spain and adjacent parts of northern Africa. All other members of this Subfamily are found in sub-Saharan Africa.

The Subfamily Colobinae is found in India and southeast Asia, but it has one Genus, *Colobus*, found in Africa south of the Sahara. This rather reciprocal relation, and especially the geographic distribution of *Macaca*, is difficult to explain on the basis of living forms. However, the fossil record helps clarify the situation.

The Colobinae are often called the "leaf-eating" monkeys for, although their diet is not restricted to leaves, they do make more use of such foods than do the other members of the Family. To utilize such a bulky diet, the Colobinae have an enlarged, sacculated stomach. Accordingly, these monkeys are highly arboreal; only one species has become semiterrestrial. They are slender animals with long extremities and a long tail. Although mainly quadrupedal and adapted to moving on top of the limbs, some show a tendency towards brachiation. The molar teeth have well-developed lophs (crests), and the lower third molar always has five cusps.

Most of the monkeys seen in zoos belong to the Subfamily Cercopithecinae, comprised of hardy animals who can withstand very adverse conditions and who are omnivorous (there is a recent report of meat eating in one species). They all have cheek pouches (lacking in Colobinae) in which they may stuff food for future mastication. Their molars have the bilophodont pattern, but the lophs (crests) are not as pronounced as in Colobinae. Also, the lower third molar may have either four or five cusps. All have a better-developed thumb than the Colobinae.

Arboreal and Semiterrestrial Cercopithecines

Most of the Cercopithecinae may be divided very generally into two groups—arboreal and semiterrestrial. The semiterrestrials—the macaques (Genus *Macaca*) and baboons (Genus *Papio*)—are short-tailed, fairly large, sexually dimorphic animals. These animals have been used so extensively in laboratories that an investigator frequently means a macaque when saying "monkeys were used as the experimental animal." There have also been more ethological or behavioral studies of this group than of others. In fact, their behavioral characteristics may be presented as if they were characteristic of all Cercopithecoidea.

Behaviorally, these are the animals who move in large troops with a dominant male at the head. They are usually territorially oriented; the males will defend the territory against others of the same species and will protect the infants and females from predators.

The more arboreal Genera are usually smaller, with less-pronounced sexual dimorphism. Being more arboreal, they have longer tails. Each species has a more restricted geographic range.

Since so few ethological investigations of the total Subfamily have been performed there is some dispute over the number of its Genera and species.[1] This diversity of opinion becomes important when an attempt is made to trace phylogenies. The classification at the end of this chapter lists eight extant Genera; five of which extend back into the Pleistocene. There is also some evidence that the Subfamily may have arisen in Miocene times. Of the extant Genera, some investigators would include *Theropithecus* (the gelada baboon) in the Genus *Papio*. Some would combine *Allenopithecus, Erythrocebus,* and *Miopithecus* with *Cercopithecus.* These are problems which additional research will resolve, but for the moment the identification of these Genera is somewhat confused.

Whether or not these are all valid Genera, the Cercopithecinae unquestionably extend back into the Pleistocene. Even so, some Genera, especially the forest-living ones, are not well represented. *Cercocebus* (the mangabey) is known from the middle Pleistocene solely by a mandible. Recently, numerous remains of *Cercopithecus* have been reported from eastern Africa, many from the same deposits which have yielded hominid remains. The evidence shows that *Cercopithecus* was becoming common in Africa between 2.9 million and 1.9 million years ago.

By contrast, the ancestry of larger, more terrestrial contemporary forms is better known in the fossil record. Whether terrestrial forms were more frequently fossilized or whether there were more of them in the past isn't clear. Also, fossils can be located more easily in nonforested areas today. And if these areas were similarly nonforested in the past, then we might expect that the semiterrestrial ancestors of contemporary open-country forms would be better represented in the fossil record.

One of the most terrestrial of the Cercopithecinae is *Theropithecus,* the gelada baboon, of Ethiopia. This monkey lives in the rock cliffs of the Abyssinian highlands and seldom, if ever, enters the trees. In many respects the gelada baboon is similar to the Genus *Papio,* which includes the common baboons of the rest of Africa. Because of this similarity some investigators do not recognize *Theropithecus* as a distinct Genus. However, taxonomic distinction seems justified since the two have probably been distinct since at least the Pliocene.

The Genus *Simopithecus* was originally established on the basis of a 1916 discovery of a mandible in Pleistocene deposits. Since then, much more material has been found

1. N. C. Tappen, "Problems of distribution and adaptation of the African monkeys," *Current Anthropology* 1 (1960):91-120.

throughout eastern and southern Africa. Based on comparative studies, most investigators would now place the *Simopithecus* material in the Genus *Theropithecus*. Furthermore, it and *Papio* are identifiably different since at least the early Pleistocene, prompting separation at the generic level. The Pleistocene *Theropithecus* is much larger than the gelada baboon, almost the size of a chimpanzee. However, its short fingers and longer upper extremity are like the gelada. These traits are looked upon as adaptations to sitting on the ground while collecting small seeds as food. The dentition is similar to that of the gelada, so these Pleistocene forms may also have been efficient seed-eaters.

Two other Pleistocene forms, *Dinopithecus* and *Gorgopithecus*, are probably close relatives of *Theropithecus*, although not as large. These have been found in South Africa, the former at Swartkrans and the latter at Kromdraai, where they were associated with the australopithecines. It is possible that man was at least partially responsible for their extinction.

From middle Pliocene deposits of northern Egypt the skull remains of a form named *Libypithecus* shows this form had a large sagittal crest, associated with large chewing muscles, and an elongated muzzle. It resembles *Theropithecus* and may well be the Pliocene ancestor of that Genus.

The Genus *Papio* includes the various species of baboons found throughout most of Africa south of the Sahara. The semiterrestrial, savannah-living forms are usually found in the trees only at night. There is pronounced sexual dimorphism, the males are considerably larger than the females (some males reaching as much as 30 kilograms). The males have especially long canines used in establishing dominance within the troop and for repelling predators. The baboons are noted for the elongation of the snout into an almost doglike muzzle.

Parapapio, known from the australopithecine sites in south Africa and from sites in east Africa, is probably the Pleistocene ancestor of *Papio*. Although the dentition of the Pleistocene Genus is essentially modern, it's muzzle is less pronounced and the bony reinforcement system of the skull less developed. Some 400 specimens have been found, and one of them was dated at 4 million years old. This would indicate that *Parapapio* was common during the Pleistocene of east and south Africa and probably extended back into the Pliocene.

All Genera of Cercopithecinae mentioned so far are found only in Africa. However, the Genus *Macaca*, also a member of the Cercopithecinae, lives in Asia today. This Genus resembles *Papio* in many morphological and biochemical ways; hybrids between these two have been bred in zoos. As a result, some investigators feel these should all be included in the Genus *Papio*. For all their resemblances, they nonetheless seem to have been separated for a long period of time.

The Macaques

The macaques are presently very widespread, from northern Japan to the Rock of Gibraltar (but never south of the Sahara). Paleontologically, they are not found south of the Sahara, even though their area of distribution during the Pleistocene may have been even broader than at present. Pleistocene remains very similar to the extant Japanese macaque (*M. fuscata*) have been reported from Japan. Remains of a very closely related Genus, *Procynocephalus*, are known from India and China. This Genus may have been even more terrestrial than is the present-day *Macaca* of India. However, during the Pleistocene, the macaques seem to have lived mainly in Europe. Numerous species have been defined from that continent with the finds ranging from

Italy (and Sardinia), through central Europe, to as far north as England. Those from the southern part of the continent are very similar to the Gibraltar species *M. sylvanus.* This species, popularly-known as the Barbary Ape, may have evolved in southern Europe.

From early Pliocene or late Miocene Algerian deposits have come remains of *M. flandrini.* This species, known from maxillary and mandibular fragments as well as numerous teeth, may have extended as far east as Egypt and may be the earliest representative of the highly adaptable Genus *Macaca.* If further finds confirm that these remains are in the Genus *Macaca,* then it would be the oldest of extant primate Genera, some 8 million years old.

Another implication of *M. flandrini* is that the macaques had their origin and early distribution in the circum-Mediterranean region. Not until later, perhaps in Pliocene times, did they move eastward into India, China, and Japan.

The Ceropithecinae are certainly a well-established and successful primate Subfamily. They seem to have been equally successful and probably as widely distributed during the Pleistocene. *M. flandrini* is the oldest known member of the Subfamily, but it seems an unlikely candidate as an ancestor for the entire Subfamily.

It is interesting to note the frequency of Cercopithecinae and Pongidae through time. Recall that it was at the end of the Miocene that the Pongidae seemed to begin their decline. At about this same time the Cercopithecinae began to increase in numbers. Whether these two events are causally related is unknown.

THE COLOBINAE

The other extant Subfamily of the Family Cercopithecidae, the Colobinae, are today centered in India and southeast Asia. Most authorities recognize six contemporary Genera, although some would not accept *Rhinopithecus* as a distinct Genus. Only one Genus, *Colobus,* is found in Africa south of the Sahara. This Subfamily is far more arboreal than the Cercopithecinae; in fact only one of its Genera, *Presbytis,* has developed semi-terrestrial habits. The Colobinae of India, where they are particularly common, are often referred to as langurs, the leaf-eating monkeys. They are not particularly common in zoos and have not often been studied or used in laboratories. As a result, their physiology, biochemistry, and even their anatomy is not as well-known as Cercopithecinae. This last fact might be somewhat surprising, considering that Galen, an influential 2d century Greek physician, did anatomical dissections of *M. sylvanus,* the Barbary Ape.

Of the extant Genera, *Colobus* remains have been found in Lower Pleistocene deposits at Olduvai Gorge along with the australopithecines. *Presbytis,* known from Early Pleistocene times in India, might have been in Europe during the Middle Pliocene if several isolated teeth actually belong to that Genus. If confirmed, the Colobinae possibly also arose in Africa and migrated to Asia through Europe.

Two fossil Genera from the Pliocene of Europe lend credence to this idea. One, *Dolichopithcus,* is known from numerous skulls and postcranial bones from southern France. This material bears a resemblance to *Colobus,* but the postcranial bones are more robust and the muzzle is more pronounced.

Based on many skulls, postcranial bones, and a complete skeleton, the other Pliocene primate Genus, *Mesopithecus,* is one of the most completely known. The main distribution seems to be centered in Greece, but remains have been found in Central Europe, the Soviet Union, and Iran. In general, the morphology of these remains is very similar to that of the langurs but indicates a larger, more robust animal. Such a physique would indicate semiterrestrial rather than strictly arboreal habits as in modern langurs. However, if these animals migrated from Africa to Asia via Europe, they could not have done so and remained arboreal. Since there were nonforested stretches to cross, one would expect some form of adaptation to terrestrial living. *Mesopithecus* may well represent this stage in the migration.

A frontal bone found in Miocene deposits of Uganda is very similar to the same bone in *Colobus.* If so, this would be the earliest remains of a colobine, indicating their origin in eastern Africa.

The third Subfamily of the Cercopithecidae, the Parapithecinae, has been extinct since Oligocene times, a time of poor preservation of primate fossils; the Fayum of Egypt is the only place where they have been found. Considering this hiatus, it is not surprising that a gap exists between the Parapithecinae and the other members of the Cercopithecidae.

The Parapithecinae are lower Oligocene in age and must be close to the time of differentiation of the Cercopithecoidea. A fused metopic suture (a single frontal bone), a fused symphysis menti (the right and left halves of the mandible fused from birth), and a bony plate separating the orbital from the temporal fossae indicate that these specimens belong to the Suborder Anthropoidea; they are not Prosimii. On the other hand, the dental formula is 2.1.3.3/2.1.3.3; they have one more premolar than the later members of the Cercopithecidae. They also lack the bilophodont molars so characteristic of all later members of that Family. Two things seem apparent. First, these are morphologically intermediate forms between earlier Prosimii (to be discussed later) and the Miocene representatives of the Cercopithecidae. The cusp pattern of the molars could easily become the bilophodont pattern found in the Miocene, while the loss of the anterior premolar would produce the typical dental formula. The second point is that if these are Oligocene Cercopithecidae, then the loss of the anterior premolar must have occurred independently in Cercopithecoidea and in the Hominoidea because the latter Superfamily had already lost that tooth.

Two Genera of Parapithecinae are recognized—*Apidium* and *Parapithecus.* The latter was established on the basis of a single mandible which unfortunately had been damaged in the incisor region. It was thought that one incisor had been lost and that the rami of the mandible met at an acute angle as in Prosimii. It was not until more complete specimens were found (now more than 40), that it was apparent that this Genus had the requisite number of teeth and the jaw form of a monkey ancestor.

The second Genus is *Apidium,* of which more than 200 specimens are known. This must have been a very successful Genus, if frequency of specimens is any indication. Although *Apidium* should be included in the Anthropoidea without reservation, the ectotympanic was not fused to the petrosal, and it may have been included within the bulla as in some modern Prosimii. This is an illustration that all traits of any taxon do not evolve at exactly the same time.

Though the cusp pattern is primitive, the there is more indication of the bilophodont pattern than in *Parapithecus.* The upper molars have additional cusps, however, and show considerable resemblance to *Oreopithecus,* probably a terminal Genus to be discussed later. It seems likely that *Apidium* is the Oligocene ancestor of *Oreopithecus,* but whether it is also ancestoral to Cercopithecidae is a question that probably will remain unresolved until specimens from the later Oligocene are available.

We must mention briefly four Genera whose exact position in the phylogeny of the monkeys is not clear. The first is *Cercopithecoides.* This Genus (from the Pleistocene) is represented by an almost complete skull and mandible from the Makapan Valley and by additional remains from other areas of South Africa. While morphologically similar to the Colobinae, this ancient monkey was a larger, more rugged animal. Since this region of Africa was savannah country during the Pleistocene this Genus may represent another invasion of open country by the Colobinae.

A skull and almost complete skeleton of a second Genus, *Paracolobus,* was found in Pliocene deposits of Kenya. Again, there is general resemblance to the Colobinae, but again this is a much larger animal with a much larger muzzle. The morphology of the teeth and jaws would indicate that it was a leaf-eater.

The third Genus is *Victoriapithecus* from the Miocene of Kenya. This Genus has a potassium-argon date of approximately 18 million years and is represented by mandibles and a few postcranial bones. Again, there are resemblances to the colobines and some indication of semiterrestrial habits, but the material is not extensive enough to make a definitive diagnosis. Interestingly enough, the lower molars are bilophodont, as are all extant Cercopithecidae molars, but the uppers are not. This could mean that this diagnostic feature of the Cercopithecidae was developing in Miocene times. (You may remember that the diagnostic criteria of the Pongidae are already established by this time.)

The last problematic Genus is *Prohylobates,* from earlier Miocene (age about 20 million years). This Genus is represented by three mandibles found in Egypt. They may possibly be related to the colobines, but they are *not* an early gibbon as once thought.

THE EXTINCT OREOPITHECOIDEA

The Suborder Catarrhini has one more Superfamily, Oreopithecoidea. It is comprised of only one Family with two possible Genera. The complex taxonomy reflects the disagreement concerning the interpretation of one of these Genera, *Oreopithecus.* The other Genus, *Mobokopithecus,* comes from the Miocene of Kenya, but since it consists solely of a lower third molar, not much can be said about it. The general morphology of the tooth could indicate an ancestoral form of *Oreopithecus.*

The original find of *Oreopithecus* was made in the latter part of the 19th century in Italy from Early Pliocene deposits. Since then many additional finds have been made, most of them from lignite deposits in Italy. Hence the common name, Abominable Coal Man, even though all agree that this is not of the Genus *Homo.* Arrangements have been made with coal miners to report any fossils encountered during the mining process. As a result, much additional material—the remains of about 50 individuals including an almost complete skeleton—have been uncovered.

Oreopithecus was about the size of a chimpanzee. It had a broad shallow chest, short lumbar region, expanded ilium, and an upper extremity longer than the lower. These are all features of present day pongids. The canine was small, there was no diastema in either jaw, and the anterior lower premolar was bicuspid. Such a combination of features led many to suggest that this form was ancestoral to the hominids. The teeth of the first specimens found were worn and the cusp pattern was indistinct. Some thought the molars had a bilophodont pattern and therefore this form should be included in the Cercopithecoidea. Later specimens had better preserved teeth, and these showed neither the bilophodont pattern nor the dryopithecine pattern of Miocene pongids. Instead, the teeth are very like the Oligocene *Apidium.* Most investigators now feel that *Oreopithecus* is probably a descendant of *Apidium* and represents another primate experimentation with brachiation. In other words, Oreopithecus represents a line of primate evolution parallel to but independent of the line leading to the Hominoidea.

SUMMARY

Today, the Cercopithecoidea—Old World monkeys—are a highly successful group, if number of Genera, species, and individuals are appropriate criteria. They are distributed widely over Africa, Asia, the islands of the western Pacific as far north as Japan. One species is even known in Europe. The fossil record seems to indicate that their great expansion took place during and after the Miocene, during the time of decline of the Pongidae. Whether this reciprocal relation is due to direct competition or to some other set of factors is as yet unknown.

Prior to the discovery of most of the fossils known today, a phyletic sequence for the Primates was based on comparative anatomy. Using such data and assuming that man is the most highly evolved of the Primates, it was logical to assume that monkeys, Cercopithecoidea, differentiated initially from a prosimian stock. Later the pongids, as man's closest relatives, differentiated, and finally man became separate. Unfortunately, the fossil record does not seem to bear out such logical assumptions. The monkeys seem to trace back to an apidiumlike ancestor of the Oligocene at which time the hallmark of the Cercopithecoidea, the bilophodont molar, had not developed. Yet at that time the ancestors of the pongids seem to be already established.

The Eocene record of the Catarrhini is not sufficiently well-known to resolve this problem, but it contains enough to raise doubts concerning the establishment of a sequence of evolution based solely on extant forms.

Classification of forms discussed in chapter 5:

- Order: Primates
  - Suborder: Anthropoidea
    - Infraorder: Catarrhini
      - Superfamily: Cercopithecoidea
        - Family: Cercopithecidae
          - Subfamily: Cercopithecinae
            - Genera: *Macaca*—Pleistocene-Recent (macaques)
              - *Cercocebus*—Pleistocene-Recent (mangabeys)
              - *Papio*—Pleistocene-Recent (baboons)
              - *Theropithecus*—Pleistocene-Recent (gelada)
              - *Cercopithecus*—Pleistocene-Recent (guenons)
              - *Allenopithecus*—Recent (Allen's monkey)
              - *Erythrocebus*—Recent (patas monkey)
              - *Miopithecus*—Recent (talapoin)
              - *Parapapio*—Pleistocene
              - *Dinopithecus*—Pleistocene
              - *Gorgopithecus*—Pleistocene
              - *Procynocephalus*—Pleistocene
              - *Libypithecus*—Pliocene
          - Subfamily: Colobinae
            - Genera: *Presbytis*—Pleistocene-Recent (langur)
              - *Pygathrix*—Recent (douc langur)
              - *Rhinopithecus*—Recent (snub-nosed langur)
              - *Simias*—Recent (Pagi

Island langur)
Nasalis—Recent
(proboscis monkey)
Colobus—Recent
(guerezas)
Mesopithecus—
Pliocene
Dolichopithecus—
Pliocene
Subfamily: Parapithecinae
Genera: *Parapithecus*—
Oligocene
Apidium—Oligocene
Family: Cercopithecidae—?
Genera: *Cercopithecoides*—
Pleistocene
Paracolobus—
Pliocene
Prohylobates—
Miocene
Victoriapithecus—
Miocene
Superfamily: Oreopithecoidea
Family: Oreopithecidae
Genera: *Oreopithecus*—
Pliocene
Mobokopithecus—
Miocene

For Further Reading

Straus, W. L. "The Classification of Oreopithecus." In *Classification and Human Evolution.* Ed. S. L. Washburn. Viking Fund Publications in Anthropology, no. 57, pp. 146-77. Chicago: Aldine Publishing Co., 1963. Contains a detailed discussion of the morphology of *Oreopithecus* and draws a conclusion in disagreement with that presented in this chapter.

Bibliography

Tappen, N. C. 1960. "Problems of distribution and adaptation of the African monkeys," *Current Anthropology* 1:91-120.

6 The Platyrrhini

The monkeys of the New World constitute the remaining Infraorder of the Suborder Anthropoidea. Found from the southern part of Mexico to the northern part of Argentina, they are essentially tropical animals, although some are found in the Andes up to about 5,000 feet. The range of adaptation is much narrower than that found among Old World Anthropoidea.

The Platyrrhini are good representatives of the Suborder Anthropoidea in that they have the complete postorbital bar and a bony plate separating the orbital from the temporal fossae. The two frontal bones fuse early in life, and the two halves of the mandible fuse in the midline at the symphysis menti. (Among the Prosimii the postorbital bar is complete, but the bony separation of the orbital and temporal fossae is absent. Also, the frontal bones in this more primitive Suborder are separate as are the two halves of the mandible.) Using these criteria, we can legitimately place the Platyrrhini in the same Suborder as the Catarrhini.

However, in some respects the Platyrrhini are intermediate between the Infraorder Catarrhini and the Suborder Prosimii. They resemble the Prosimii in that they retain three premolars (Catarrhini have only two); the ectotympanic is not extended laterally (in Catarrhini this lateral extension forms a bony canal for the external opening of the ear), and the bulla of the middle ear is inflated (Catarrhini lack an inflated bulla). Some investigators have felt that the presence of these primitive traits indicated that the Platyrrhini probably had an origin among the Prosimii independent of that of the Catarrhini. If so, then the Platyrrhini should not be included in the Suborder Anthropoidea. This question will be discussed later.

TRAITS OF THE NEW WORLD MONKEYS

The most easily observable external traits separating the Platyrrhini and Catarrhini are: 1. The Platyrrhini have a wide internasal septum so that the nostrils open more laterally than inferiorly. Among the Catarrhini the internasal septum is narrow and the nostrils open caudally. 2. The Platyrrhini thumb is not as highly differentiated. The thumb (when present) has two phalanges, but it lacks even the degree of efficiency found in the Cercopithecoidea. These New World monkeys lack a precision grip. In some groups grasping is quite different from that found in Old World taxa; that is, in some the thumb and first finger work together and oppose the other three digits; in other Primates the grasp is between the thumb on one side and all four fingers on the other. 3. Although the Platyrrhini have technically flat nails, the nail in cross section looks more tentlike and is almost a pseudoclaw. 4. All Platyrrhini lack cheek pouches, ischial callosities, and an externally apparent menstrual cycle.

As in all Anthropoidea, the Platyrrhini incisors are nipping teeth. The canines are variable in size; they are large in some species but hardly extend beyond the occlusal plane in others. The premolars are bicuspid teeth with the anterior one being the largest. Unlike that of the Prosimii, the most posterior premolar is never molariform. Usually, the upper premolars have two roots, the lowers only one. The molars may have four cusps and decrease in size from front to back. In one taxon, the third molar is missing, a unique feature among the primates. On the occlusal surface of the molars an enamel loph may connect two cusps, but a true bilophodont molar is absent.

In general, the Platyrrhini are small animals; the largest is *Alouatta* (the howler monkey) where the males may reach a little over seven kilograms and the females a bit less than six kilograms. *Cebuella,* the pygmy marmoset, is the smallest of the Anthropoidea. Failure to develop large-bodied taxa is undoubtedly a reflection of the universal arboreal habitat of these animals. Remember that among Old World Anthropoidea, only semiterrestrial forms reach large body size. It seems strange that no semiterrestrial forms have evolved among these South American primates. There were open savannahs capable of invasion especially since there were fewer predators in the New World to discourage the move. Yet there is no evidence that any of the Platyrrhini have ever attempted terrestrial living. Simply because an ecological niche is available apparently is no assurance that it will be occupied.

Although the Platyrrhini are readily distinguished from the Catarrhini and have not adapted to as wide a range of niches as the latter, a satisfactorily detailed classification of these monkeys has never been devised. Most authorities recognize only one Superfamily, the Ceboidea, containing three Families—Cebidae, Callithricidae, and Xenothricidae, this last being extinct. At the Subfamily level there is even less unanimity of opinion. Three factors seem responsible for this. First, extant forms have not received the detailed study given Old World taxa. Second, the fossil record is very incomplete; highly arboreal, tropical animals are not as likely to be as well represented in the fossil record as savannah forms. Third, there have been fewer qualified investigators interested in these South American primates.

The Family Callithricidae includes the monkeys popularly known as marmosets and tamarins. Unfortunately, these popular names have been applied outside this Family so one must be careful in correlating popular with taxonomic names. All the Genera in this Family are very small highly arboreal animals, with long, furry, nonprehensile tails. Unique among primates, they have lost the third molar; their dental formula is 2.1.3.2/2.1.3.2 = 32. The great toe has a flat nail, but all other digits have a long, clawlike nail (a true claw, according to some authorities). If so, these are the only Anthropoidea who lack nails on all digits. They have a smooth-surfaced brain and normally give birth to twins. The forelimb is shorter than the hindlimb; hands and feet are very long; and scent glands are in the genital region. Furthermore, these are the only Anthropoidea with only three cusps on the upper molars. In all this is a strange combination of primitive and advanced traits. After reviewing their anatomy Hershkovitz concludes that these are the most primitive of living monkeys.[1] He feels they must have

1. P. Hershkovitz, "Notes on Tertiary platyrrhine monkeys and description of a new Genus from the late Miocene of Columbia." Folia primatologica, 12 (1970):1-37.

been separated from the rest of the platyrrhines for a long time. On the other hand, Bender and Chu, after studying their chromosomes, conclude from chromosomal studies that they are a specialized group and not at all primitive.[2] Other authorities fall in between these extremes. The fact that the Callithricidae are completely unknown in the fossil record does not help the situation.

The Family Xenothricidae presents more of a problem than even the Callithricidae. This Family is known from a single mandible found in Pleistocene deposits on the island of Jamaica, the only fossil primate uncovered from a Carribbean Island. The dental formula is ?/2.1.3.2; at least in the lower jaw the formula is like the Callithricidae. For the size of the mandible, the molars are large and the crown pattern resembles that of the Cebidae. The incisors are procumbent, and the canine is small. Because of such a strange mixture of traits, the exact position of *Xenothrix* in the phylogeny of the platyrrhines is unknown. It certainly indicates that much more will have to be known about the fossil record of platyrrhines before a reasonably accurate picture is possible.

MOST PLATYRRHINES ARE CEBIDS

The great majority of platyrrhines belong to the Family Cebidae. Although seven Subfamilies will be recognized here, this does not represent the unanimous opinion of workers in the field. The two Subfamilies Alouattinae and Atelinae are rather similar in that both have a long, well-developed, prehensile tail. The Alouattinae is represented by a single Genus, *Alouatta,* the howler monkey. Atelinae has three Genera, *Ateles* (the spider monkey), *Lagothrix* (the woolly monkey), and *Brachyteles* (the woolly-spider monkey). These last three Genera are rather large for platyrrhines, but *Alouatta* is even larger. The most outstanding feature of this latter Genus is the tremendous development of the hyoid-laryngeal apparatus and the associated expansion of the angular region of the mandible. This development makes loud howling possible. The howling is used behaviorally as a spacing mechanism to keep different troops from occupying the same territory simultaneously. Development of the "howling" mechanism has produced distinctive changes in the total morphology of the skull. Two features, however, probably are not associated with this howling specialization. The first is a large foramen in the zygomatic (cheek) bone through which a large bundle of nerves and blood vessels passes to the face. The second is the absence of an entepicondylar foramen on the humerus. Pleistocene deposits hold the earliest trace of the Genus *Alouatta.*

Although the Subfamily Atelinae does not have the tremendous development of the hyoid-laryngeal apparatus as in Alouattinae, there is an expansion of the mandibular angle and a large foramen in the zygomatic bone. Like Alouattinae the canines are small. In one Genus, *Ateles,* the phalanges of the thumb are missing. A species of the Genus *Bracheteles* has been found in Pleistocene cave deposits in Brazil. These remains consist of some long bones and teeth, which though larger than the average of the extant species, may not be outside the range of variation of that species. Even if this should be true (that this is a distinct species), the Atelinae like the Alouattinae cannot be traced prior to the Pleistocene.

The subfamily Pithecinae today includes three Genera: *Pithecia, Cacajao,* and *Chiro-*

2. M. A. Bender and E. H. Y. Chu, "The chromosomes of primates," In *Evolution and Genetic Biology of Primates,* J. Buettner-Janusch, ed., vol. 1 (New York: Academic Press, 1963), pp. 261-310.

potes. These are moderately sized animals with long or short tails (*Cacajao* is short-tailed). When long, the tail is very bushy, but in either case the tail is never prehensile. The internasal septum is the widest of any platyrrhine, and the grasp is between the thumb and first finger on one side against the other three fingers (also found in *Lagothrix*). The incisors are very long, somewhat procumbent, and separated from the large canine by a diastema. The lower incisors are compressed laterally but do not form a typical dental comb as seen in the Prosimii. In the mandible there is a second diastema separating the canine from the anterior premolar. The canines are triangular in cross section and hollow.

Portions of a skull, mandible, and post-cranial bones of a platyrrhine monkey—placed in the Genus *Cebupithecia*—were found in Late Miocene deposits of Colombia. According to one investigator, these remains present the morphological characteristics of the Pithecinae. More recently, Hershkovitz has reexamined them and concludes that resemblances to Pithecinae are due to distortion during fossilization.[3] In reviewing the teeth he finds significant differences from Pithecinae (cheek teeth lack wrinkling; upper canines are round-based and not hollow as in extant Pithecinae). Hershkovitz feels that these traits call for placing *Cebupithecia* in its own Subfamily, a course followed here. With this classification, the Pithecinae are unknown prior to the Recent epoch, and we have another Subfamily which followed its own course of evolution until it became extinct sometime after the Miocene.

Callimico, an "Aberrant"

Another Subfamily, Callimiconinae, contains only one Genus, *Callimico,* or Goeldi's tamarin or marmoset. Some authors prefer not to recognize this Subfamily. Instead, they erect a separate Family, Callimiconidae for this single Genus, which is unknown in the fossil record. However one wishes to classify these strange platyrrhines, they present a combination of traits which, on the whole, place them intermediate between the Families Cebidae and Callithricidae. Because of the lack of paleontological depth for this Genus, it cannot be determined whether it is another aberrant form or the survival of a stock from which both the Cebidae and Callithricidae diverged. Bender and Chu on the basis of the karyotype, feel that this is a primitive group representing the survival of an ancestoral stock.[4] Other evidence, however, does not seem to bear out their conclusion.

Callimico is a small monkey about the size of the other marmosets and tamarins. It has a flat nail on the great toe, but other digits have marmosetlike "claws." The occlusal pattern of the molar teeth is like the Callithricidae, but unlike them the dental formula is 2.1.3.3/2.1.3.3, a resemblance to the Cebidae. The general morphology of the mandible and placement of the incisor teeth is cebidlike, but the maxilla is vertically short making it more like the Prosimii than the other platyrrhines. Again, we have a strange combination of traits defying a neat classification. However, if we view the biological world as a continuum in time and remember that the only naturally real taxon is the species (all others are manmade), then such forms would occasionally be found. Our understanding of the reasons for such difficulties in classification would be helped with a more complete fossil record.

3. P. Hershkovitz, "Notes on Tertiary platyrrhine monkeys."

4. Bender and Chu, "The chromosomes of primates."

The Cebinae

The Subfamily Cebinae consists of medium-sized animals with long tails and prominent faces. The internasal septum is not as wide as in Pithecinae; the hyoid-laryngeal apparatus is not inflated as in Alouattinae. The thumb, fairly well-developed for a platyrrhine, maintains a grasp between it and the four fingers. The incisors are set vertically in the jaws, and the third molar is the smallest of the molar series.

The Subfamily has 2 extant Genera which differ considerably in details other than those listed above. The first Genus, *Cebus* (capuchins, or organ-grinder monkeys), resembles the Alouattinae and Atelinae in having a prehensile tail but differs because the tip of its tail is hairy instead of naked. The general form of the skull is similar to that in Pithecinae and Atelinae with the upper incisors set vertically and the lowers somewhat procumbently. In the upper jaw there is a wide diastema between the lateral incisor and the canine. The premolars are larger than the molars; the third molars are small.

The other Genus, *Saimiri* (squirrel monkey), is smaller in body size, lacks a prehensile tail, but has an enlarged neurocranium as compared to the face. In fact the neurocranium size/facial size ratio is not only larger in *Saimiri* than in *Cebus* but is also larger than in *Homo*. The face is flat and less prognathous than in *Cebus*. Coupled with this orientation of the face, the foramen magnum is more inferiorly directed. The upper canines are large and sexually dimorphic. A diastema exists anterior to the upper canine, but there is none in the lower jaw. The post-canine teeth are in parallel rows. The orbits, large for a diurnal animal, are set close together; the interorbital septum is incompletely ossified resulting in a large foramen connecting the two orbital cavities in the skull. Such a foramen is lacking in *Cebus* and other platyrrhines.

Although *Saimiri* is often considered a rather primitive, unspecialized cebid, it is unknown prior to the Recent epoch. *Cebus* is known from Pleistocene deposits, but there are no antecedents in the Pliocene. A mandible found in deposits from the Late Miocene of Colombia was designated *Neosaimiri.* This mandible is very similar to that of *Saimiri* with some minor differences. The rows of cheek teeth diverge posteriorly, and the third molars have not been reduced in size. There are also some differences in the cusp patterns of the teeth. On the whole, this mandible is very similar to that found in the living Genus.

Also from Miocene deposits in Colombia comes the Genus *Stirtonia.* This is the largest known fossil platyrrhine mandible, about the size of that of a female *Alouatta.* It is V-shaped so that the cheek teeth diverge posteriorly. The incisors are small and crowded. In these respects it is like some Prosimii. The canines, however, are well-developed. Some authors see an antecedent-like resemblance between *Stirtonia* and the Cebinae, but Hershkovitz would place it in its own Subfamily.[5] Whether this form is related to any living one or not is an open question, but its resemblances seem to be most marked with the Oligocene *Apidium* of the African Fayum.

The Aotinae

The remaining Subfamily, Aotinae, perhaps has two Genera, *Aotus* and *Callicebus.* But as with the Cebinae, some authorities would place these in separate Subfamilies. These are small animals with long furry, nonprehensile tails, and short faces. The lower extremity is longer than the upper and the dentition is primitive. The incisors are moderately spatulate (they are not com-

5. Hershkovitz, "Notes on Tertiary platyrrhine monkeys."

pressed laterally as in Prosimii), the canines are small, and there is no diastema. The lower premolars are simple teeth although the uppers are bicuspid. The molars have four cusps; the third molar is the smallest. Essentially, *Aotus* differs from *Callicebus* in being the only nocturnal anthropoid. As a result, the orbits in *Aotus* are very large, encroaching to such a degree on the maxilla that it has become shallow as in Prosimii. The enlargement of the orbits probably also accounts for the unusually wide communication between the orbital and temporal fossae. The zygomatic foramen is large. *Aotus* is unknown prior to the Recent epoch; *Callicebus* is known from the Pleistocene, but like the Cebinae there are no Pliocene remains.

The Genus *Homunculus* has been uncovered from Miocene deposits. This Genus is known from numerous finds, some from the southern part of Patagonia and others from Colombia. The Patagonian remains are apparently a bit older than the more northern ones. The skull remains show that there was a postorbital bar and a bony wall separating the orbital and temporal fossae. The remains also indicate that a tympanic bulla was present, but they are not complete enough to indicate its detailed structure. There is a large zygomatic foramen and the humerus has an entepicondylar foramen. Thus it seems evident that this is an early platyrrhine. The general morphology of the mandible has led most authorities to align this fossil with Aotinae, but the expansion of the angular region of the mandible has led others to feel it is closer to Alouattinae. On the other hand, the mandible is narrow anteriorly and diverges posteriorly, like *Stirtonia* and the Prosimii. Also, the interorbital region is wide (an unplatyrrhine trait), and the lacrimal foramen is outside the orbit, another resemblance to the Prosimii.

Homunculus is preceded in the Oligocene by *Dolichocebus* from Argentina. This Genus consists of a broken cranium; the dental formula was 2.1.3.3/? and the third molar was the smallest. The general morphology is very similar to *Homunculus*. Radinsky, after examining the endocast, was able to show that the visual cortex is expanded over that of the prosimians, indicating an anthropoid shift to reliance on vision as opposed to smell.[6]

A brief word must be said about another Genus, *Branisella,* based on a left maxillary bone from the Oligocene of Bolivia. Although it is a platyrrhine of the Superfamily Ceboidea, its more detailed classification is impossible. The teeth are generalized and could be ancestoral to any of the subsequent platyrrhines. It also bears some resemblances to *Apidium* of the Fayum.

ORIGINS OF THE PLATYRRHINES

Looking at the Platyrrhini as a whole, it is apparent that they possess the criteria for inclusion in the Suborder Anthropoidea. By implication, this means that they and the Old World higher primates had a common ancestor who at some time diverged from a prosimian ancestor. Unlike their Old World relatives the platyrrhines have remained highly arboreal and restricted almost entirely to the New World tropics. Within this zone, however, they have diverged considerably. In some cases they have retained more resemblances to their prosimian ancestors than did their African and Asian relatives, while in other cases they perfected arboreal adaptations unknown elsewhere among the Primates (prehensile tails, for example). Prehensile tails are of course not restricted to platyrrhines; it is noteworthy that a number of other

6. L. Radinsky, "The fossil evidence of anthropoid brain evolution," *American Journal of Physical Anthropology* 41 (1974):15-27.

South American mammals have moved in a similar direction.

Apparently the divergencies seen among the platyrrhines developed within their present geographic range. The lack of detailed studies of their skeletal morphology in all but a few of the Genera makes it difficult to establish a useful classification. In fact, many extant Genera and species are defined on the basis of pelage coloration, a characteristic not preserved in the fossil record.

Another inhibiting factor in the study of South American primates is the fact that arboreal populations tend to have restricted ranges and to interbreed less with adjacent populations than do terrestrial populations. Over a period of time, one would expect that these arboreal populations would gradually drift apart and acquire minor differences not apparent in living specimens in the same taxon. Recent studies of karyotypes seem to indicate that some long-recognized species may really be separate in the senses that different populations are incapable of producing fertile hybrids. Much more work needs to be done, especially in the area of ethology, before a final classification becomes possible.

The fact that less than a dozen fragmentary fossils are known is no great help in our understanding of the platyrrhines. In this review most of these fossils have been placed in extant Subfamilies, but many students of the platyrrhines feel that this is incorrect. They see no antecedents for extant Genera in the fossil record. In brief, our present knowledge of the South American primates is unsatisfactory.

Considering these uncertainties, it is not surprising that attempts to locate the prosimian ancestor of the Playrrhini have not met with universal success. As will be discussed later, since the earliest prosimians are found in North America, it seemed logical to assume that the origin of the platyrrhines would be found among these North American forms. What little is known of the fossil record indicated that this separation must have occurred in Early Oligocene times at the latest. It was known that the land surfaces of North and South America were not connected before the Pleistocene so that if the platyrrhines originated in North America some form of rafting between islands must have taken place. It was assumed that during early Cenozoic times North and South America had been in much their present relation to one another.

Role of "Continental Drift"

During the 1950s and 1960s the concept of "floating continents" became firmly established. It is now well established that South America separated from Africa around the opening of the Cenozoic and remained close to that continent for some period of time. Later, North America separated from Europe. Making use of these recent developments in geology, Hoffstetter has proposed that not only the platyrrhines but also the caviomorph rodents (today found only in South America) had their origin in Africa and that during the Late Eocene they rafted across the narrow south Atlantic.[7] This hypothesis also requires crossing a body of water, and, in this regard, his hypothesis is very similar to that of a North American origin. However, the African origin has the advantage, for it would not only account for the platyrrhines but also for South American rodents (both groups resemble early African fauna).[8]

7. R. Hoffstetter, "Relationships, origins, and history of the ceboid monkeys and caviomorph rodents: A modern reinterpretation," In *Evolutionary Biology,* T. Dobzhansky, T.M.K. Hecht, and W. C. Steere, eds., vol. 6 (New York: Appleton-Century-Crofts, 1972), pp. 323-47.

8. For other faunal resemblances between Africa and South America, see Fooden, "Breakup of Pangaea."

If the North American origin of the Platyrrhini is accepted, as many still do, then one is faced with explaining the resemblances between the Platyrrhini and Catarrhini. The usual explanation is that this is an example of convergent evolution; that is, that by adapting to similar environments, forms once different came to look alike. In this case, then, there is no justification for the Suborder Anthropoidea because its two Infraorders would have had independent origins within the Prosimii.

If, on the other hand, the African origin of the platyrrhines is accepted, they would have had a common origin with the catarrhines from the prosimians and their combination in the Anthropoidea is phylogenetically justified; their common traits are due to common heritage. Such an assumption helps in understanding the resemblances between early South American fossils, *Homunculus, Stirtonia, Branisella,* and *Apidium* from the African Fayum. This is not to say that *Apidium* is directly ancestoral to the Platyrrhini, since *Apidium, Dolichocebus,* and *Branisella* all stem from Oligocene times. The assumption of African origin would imply that these Genera are close to the common ancestor who was probably at least of Eocene age.

SUMMARY

Our understanding of the Platyrrhini—South American monkeys—needs improvement. Details of the extant forms are not well known and few fossils are available to help in establishing a phylogeny. Based on morphological resemblances, the Platyrrhini and Catarrhini are together placed in the Suborder Anthropoidea. Many authorities explain these resemblances as due to parallel evolution. This implies that these Infraorders arose separately from prosimian ancestors. But if the Platyrrhini are descended directly from an early North American prosimian, there is no justification for the Suborder Anthropoidea. If, on the other hand, the Hoffstetter hypothesis is accepted, and we assume that the Platyrrhini got to South America via Africa, then the Suborder is justified. This interpretation would make understandable the slight resemblances of early platyrrhines to the Oligocene *Apidium* of Africa. We would have to recognize that *Apidium* itself was somewhat closer to the common ancestor, probably Eocene in age.

Classification of forms discussed in chapter 6:

- Order: Primates
  - Suborder: Anthropoidea
    - Infraorder: Platyrrhini
      - Superfamily: Ceboidea
        - Family: Cebidae
          - Subfamily: Aotinae
            - Genera: *Aotus*—Recent (owl monkey)
              Callicebus—Pleistocene-Recent (titi)
              Homunculus—Miocene
              Dolichocebus—Oligocene
          - Subfamily: Pithecinae
            - Genera: *Cacajao*—Recent (uakaris)
              Pithecia—Recent (saki monkey)
              Chiropotes—Recent (saki monkey)
          - Subfamily: Alouattinae
            - Genus: *Alouatta*—Pleistocene-Recent (howler)
          - Subfamily: Cebinae
            - Genera: *Cebus*—Pleistocene-Recent (capuchins)
              Saimiri—Recent (squirrel monkey)
              Neosaimiri—Miocene
              Stirtonia—Miocene

Subfamily: Atelinae
Genera: *Ateles*—Recent (spider monkey)
Lagothrix—Recent (woolly monkey)
Brachyteles— Recent (woolly spider monkey)
Subfamily: Callimiconinae
Genus: *Callimico*—Recent (Goeldi's marmoset)
Subfamily: Cebupithecinae
Genus: *Cebupithecia*—Miocene
Family: Callithricidae
Genera: *Callithrix*—Recent (marmosets)
Saguinas—Recent (tamarins)
Family: Xenothricidae
Genus: *Xenothrix*—Pleistocene
Superfamily: Ceboidea?
Genus: *Branisella*—Oligocene

For Further Reading

Orlosky, F. J. and D. R. Swindler. "Origins of New World monkeys." *Journal of Human Evolution* 4 (1975):77-83. These authors do not agree with the idea of an African origin of the New World monkeys.

Bibliography

Bender, M. A. and E. H. Y. Chu. 1963. "The chromosomes of primates." In *Evolution and Genetic Biology of Primates*." ed. J. Buettner-Janusch. Vol. 1. New York: Academic Press, pp. 261-310.

Fooden, J. 1972. "Breakup of Pangaea and isolation of relic mammals in Australia, South America, and Madagascar. *Science* 175:894-98.

Hershkovitz, P. 1970. "Notes on Tertiary platyrrhine monkeys and description of a new genus from the late Miocene of Columbia." *Folia primatologica* 12:1-37.

Hoffstetter, R. 1972. Relationships, origins, and history of the ceboid monkeys and caviomorph rodents: A modern reinterpretation." In *Evolutionary Biology* eds. T. Dobzhansky, T.M.K. Hecht, and W. C. Steere. Vol. 6. New York: Appleton-Century-Crofts, pp. 323-47.

Radinsky, L. 1974. "The fossil evidence of anthropoid brain evolution." *American Journal of Physical Anthropology* 41:15-27.

7 The Prosimii

In the discussion of contemporary primates in chapter 1, it was pointed out that they could be placed in one of two Suborders—Prosimii or Anthropoidea. When talking about primates in general we usually think about the Anthropoidea—monkeys and apes. Though a mistake, it is probably made because the Prosimii are not common in zoos; they have not been used in research as extensively as the Anthropoidea; and they do not make good pets (nor do most primates). However, because the Prosimii are in many respects intermediate between the Order Insectivora and the Anthropoidea, and, because they are very common in deposits of early Cenozoic age, they are of considerable importance for an understanding of primate phylogeny and, ultimately, of man's place in that phylogeny.

A general view of the geologic history of the Prosimii can be gained from table 7.1. Note that most authorities recognize almost 80 Genera in this Suborder. Obviously we cannot specifically discuss all of these in this short review. Note also that prosimian Genera are most frequent during the Eocene; during the middle part of the Cenozoic they become rare; but during the Recent period they have a resurgence. A number of things should be kept in mind when viewing a table of this nature. The Paleocene and Eocene Genera are often based on very fragmentary remains; subsequent discoveries may well show that at least some of these Genera should be combined. That is, early Prosimii may not have been as diversified as this table seems to indicate. At the same time, remember that the lack of Genera during the middle Cenozoic is really negative evidence; very few have been found, but this doesn't necessarily mean they were not there. Many living Prosimii are very small, nocturnal animals. If this was also true during the earlier epochs, they would not likely be fossilized or, if fossilized, would be difficult to find. Certainly the

TABLE 7.1. NUMBER OF PROSIMII GENERA BY GEOLOGIC EPOCH*

Epoch	Number of Genera
Recent	16
Subrecent	4
Pleistocene	2
Pliocene	1
Miocene	3
Oligocene	1
Eocene	37
Paleocene	14
Cretaceous	1
Total	79

*Genera are counted in the epoch in which they first appear. The Genera listed as Subrecent are known Post-Pleistocene but are now extinct.

great increase during the Recent epoch might well indicate that living Prosimii are easier to locate than fossil ones.

LIVING PROSIMIANS

The living Prosimii are divided into three Infraorders: Lemuriformes, Lorisiformes, and Tarsiiformes. The first and last of these are known from the Eocene, but the Lorisiformes are not known prior to the Miocene. An extinct Infraorder, Plesiadapiformes, is known from the Cretaceous, Paleocene, and Eocene; it bridges the gap between the Primates and Insectivora.

Tarsius

As far as its one living Genus is concerned, the Infraorder Tarsiiformes is almost a connecting link between the Prosimii and the Anthropoidea. In fact some authors do not consider this living Genus, *Tarsius,* to be a prosimian. Unlike the other Prosimii, the canal for the external ear is bony, the frontals are fused into one bone, and the halves of the mandible are also fused. In these respects *Tarsius* is like the Anthropoidea. The back wall to the orbit, although larger than in other prosimians, is not yet at the anthropoid level, the teeth are primitive, and claws are retained on two digits of the foot. The dental formula is 2.1.3.3/1.1.3.3.

Tarsius is a small, furry animal, nocturnal and arboreal. The orbits are very large, as might be expected from its nocturnal habits, and frontally located so that they impinge on the nose, which is very small and lacks a rhinarium. Its jumping mode of progression is reflected in the elongation of some of the tarsal bones (hence the name) and in the fusion of the distal portions of the tibia and fibula (a condition unique among primates). Also as part of its jumping mode of locomotion, there are suction pads on the digits.

The combination of prosimian and anthropoid traits in this little primate has engendered considerable discussion as to its significance in primate phylogeny. These discussions, although interesting and at times ingenious, have not been particularly profitable because of the hiatus in the fossil record. *Tarsius* itself is unknown prior to the Recent period. In fact, we must go all the way back to the Eocene before any close relatives are found. These are usually placed in the Subfamily Microchoerinae, European forms that show many features later found in *Tarsius.* Such features include large orbits, a short muzzle, a triangular palate, and teeth almost identical to those of *Tarsius.* The bony, back wall of the orbit is not as complete as in *Tarsius,* but the formation of the external auditory canal from the ectotympanic is almost the same. Based on similarities in morphology, the Microchoerinae seem logical ancestors for *Tarsius,* but it must be remembered that there are no connecting fossils after the Eocene.

Closely allied to the Microchoerinae is the Family Anaptomorphidae, known from the Eocene to the Miocene with Genera in both North America and Europe. Although more primitive than *Tarsius,* the Genera included in this Family show some striking resemblances and some significant differences. The orbits are large; the muzzle is narrow; and the brain case is wide and round. The bulla has a formation similar to *Tarsius,* and the cheek-teeth pattern is almost the same. Some Genera show specializations precluding them as direct ancestors of the extant Genus. Thus some but not all have lost the anterior premolar, so that the dental formula, at least in the mandible, is ?/2.1.2.3. Others have lost one or two incisor teeth. A cranial endocast of one Eocene Genera shows that the olfactory lobes are still large and the frontal lobes small. Thus it appears that smell was still an important sense in this animal. Another endocast from an Oligocene Genera shows reduction in the olfactory and enlargement of the visual areas to about the same level as *Tarsius.*

Undoubtedly, somewhere in these Eocene Tarsiiformes is the ancestor of *Tarsius* but not enough is known to be specific. It seems apparent that during this early period many mutations were being retained. These ultimately led to a variety of specific adaptations, all but one of which became extinct at least by the Miocene.

Three fragmentary Eocene Genera—one from Europe and two from China—should be mentioned even though their exact position within the Tarsiiformes is not known. Although they tell us little about morphology and probably left no descendants of any significance, they do indicate that tarsiiform primates have dispersed across the Northern Hemisphere by the end of the Eocene.

The Lorisiformes today are small, nocturnal animals found in southern Asia and Africa south of the Sahara. Their orbits are large; the face is short; and the ectotympanic forms a bony external auditory meatus. In these respects there is a resemblance to *Tarsius*. However, a rhinarium is present and the bony wall separating the orbital from the temporal fossa is absent. The dental formula is 2.1.3.3/2.1.3.3 as in most other prosimians and in platyrrhine monkeys. The lower incisors and canines are procumbent, assuming an almost horizontal position, and because of lateral compression, form a "dental comb." In *Tarsius* the anterior teeth are set vertically in the mandible, and a "dental comb" is absent.

Galago

The contemporary forms may be divided into two Subfamilies, one of which, the Galaginae, consists of a single Genus, *Galago.* These are active animals with an elongated tarso-metatarsal region of the foot, a jumping adaptation. South of the Sahara in Africa they occupy much the same ecological niche as *Tarsius* occupies in south Asia. However, in *Galago* the eyes are more laterally placed; the nose has not been reduced to the same degree; and suction pads for the digits are absent. *Galago* is unknown in the fossil record.

THE LORISES

The second Subfamily, Lorisinae, is found today in southern Asia and Africa south of the Sahara. These differ from *Galago* in that the orbits are directed more forward and upward; the nasal region is narrower; and the palate is shorter and broader. Not only is the jumping adaptation absent, but these animals move very slowly. The second digit is much reduced in size, and the powerful grip is between the thumb and fourth digit. The tail is extremely short.

The Lorisinae, like the Galaginae, are unknown from the Pleistocene, but one of its Genera, *Indraloris,* has been found in Pliocene and Miocene deposits of India. Only a lower second molar and an incomplete mandible have been found.

Two other Genera, *Progalago* and *Komba,* have been discovered in Miocene deposits of Kenya. Remains of the former include the facial portion of a skull, but the latter is known only from mandibles. These are certainly Lorisiformes and are likely in the Subfamily Galaginae. If so, then these two Subfamilies must have separated sometime prior to the Miocene. In any event, these two plus *Indraloris* show that the Lorisiformes trace back at least to the Miocene.

THE LEMURS

The remaining extant Infraorder of the Prosimii is the Lemuriformes. Usually considered the most primitive of living prosimians, its members are confined to Madagascar and the adjacent Comoro Islands. Just when the primates invaded these islands isn't known, but it was after Madagascar separated from the mainland of Africa (some form of rafting must have been used), and before the Anthropoidea became established in eastern Africa. No members of the Anthropoidea other than *Homo sapiens* are known from Madagascar or the Comoros. It isn't even known whether this migration occurred just once, or if a number of them took place. Certainly today the Lemuriformes are a highly diversified group with a number of very aberrant forms. In their island retreats, the Lemuriformes have never been in competition with Anthropoidea and have had contact with only a few rodents. Probably for these reasons they retain diurnal forms (note that all other extant Prosimii are nocturnal). Also, it is only within the Lemuriformes that a semiterrestrial adaptation exists today.

Like the Lorisiformes, the Lemuriformes retain separate frontal bones, an unfused symphysis menti, no partition between the orbital and temporal fossae, a dental comb, and three premolars (in most forms). They also retain the rhinarium, indicating that smell is still an important sense. They also retain vibrissae (sensory hairs) on the face. Some forms have these hairs also on the upper extremity.

Unlike that of the Lorisiformes, the ectotympanic does not form a bony ear canal but instead is contained within the bulla. The face is more elongated or doglike, and the cranial base lacks the angle at the sella turcica that develops as the face migrates under the cranium during growth.

All living Lemuriformes are usually placed in a single Superfamily, Lemuroidea, which assumes they all have a common ancestor separate from the other Infraorders. If, however, there were a number of migrations to these islands, they may not have had a common ancestor. Again, we have an unanswerable question due to the paucity of the fossil record. None of the Lemuroidea are known prior to the Pleistocene, and even in the Pleistocene, the record is incomplete. It is known that during the Pleistocene, the Lemuroidea developed some now-extinct giant forms. Reaching the body size of a large dog those forms also had enormous heads. It is possible that the human invasion of Madagascar brought about their extinction.

During the Pliocene and Miocene, Lemuriformes are unknown, but in the Oligocene and Eocene the Family Adapidae is well represented. Two Subfamilies are recognized—Adapinae (European) and Notharctinae (North American). The former has one Genus that extends into the Oligocene, but otherwise both Subfamilies are Eocene in age.

THE ADAPIDAE—PRIMITIVE PROSIMIANS

The Adapidae were a group of primitive prosimians, each member had a small brain and a relatively large face. The mandible had a broad ascending ramus which, with the well-developed sagittal crest, indicates large muscles of mastication. The small orbits probably indicate that these forms were not nocturnal, and the lacrymal bone and its lacrymal foramen lies within the orbital cavity. The postorbital bar is complete except in *Pronycticebus*. The dental formula is 2.1.4.3/2.1.4.3 showing that these primates had not yet lost the first premolar; recall that no extant primate has more than three premolars (four premolars are present in the earliest mammals). The teeth are set adjacent in the bone so that there are no diastema even though the canines are fairly well developed. The incisors are set vertically in the jaws; there is no indication of a dental comb.

There are resemblances to the Lemuridae

in that the ectotympanic is free within the bulla and does not form a bony external auditory canal. Details of the course of the internal carotid and stapedial arteries and of the structure of the cochlea are the same in both Families. Because of these resemblances most authorities feel that it was from the Adapidae that subsequent Lemuriformes may have developed, despite the fact that the Adapidae are unknown in Africa. Gingerich sees no reason why they should not be considered ancestoral to the higher primates.[1]

EXTINCT PROSIMIANS

The three Infraorders of Prosimii discussed so far all have living Genera, but the fourth Infraorder, Plesiadapiformes, is wholly extinct. In fact, no Genera of this Infraorder is known after the Eocene. Most Genera are Paleocene, but one extends back into the Cretaceous and becomes the only recognized primate prior to the Cenozoic. Four Families of Plesiadapiformes are usually recognized.

The Plesiadapidae are known from Paleocene and Eocene times and from both North America and Europe. There is a rather sizable group of skulls, mandibles, and parts of the postcranial skeleton. Since the bulla is formed from the petrosal bone, they are considered Primates, but the postorbital bar is incomplete. Though this bar is complete in all living Primates its absence in early members of the order can be expected. Also expected is their possession of claws instead of nails on the digits. This Family is not ancestoral to any subsequent primates as it lost certain teeth retained in later Genera. The central incisors are hypertrophied; the lateral incisors have been lost along with the canines and lower premolars; and only one upper premolar remains. A structure, such as a tooth, once lost cannot be regained; as a result, these early primates represent an aberrant adaptation which not only took them off the main line of primate evolution, but also led to early extinction.

Much the same picture holds for the second Family, Carpolestidae. This Family is not as well known, but mandibles and partial skulls are available. Restricted to North America, the Family extends from the Paleocene into the Eocene. The upper dental formula is not known for certain but the lower is probably ?/1.1.2.3, again showing the loss of teeth present in later Genera. The single incisor is large and procumbent, but the most characteristic tooth is the last premolar—bladelike with numerous cusps. This Family represents another early adaptation of the Primates quickly to become extinct.

The Picrodontidae are known from mandibles and a cranium from the Paleocene of North America. The lower central incisor is very large and procumbent with a knifelife edge. The canine is small, and the premolars are highly specialized, having a flat occlusal surface apparently adapted to crushing pulpy foods. Again, there is no indication that these forms contributed to later primate evolution.

The final Family, Paromomyidae, of North America is very likely the group from which later primates evolved, but unfortunately it is the least well known. The earliest Genera, from Cretaceous times, is known only from teeth. Study of Paleocene and Eocene forms indicate a probable dental formula of 2.1.3.3/2.1.3.3, with the only specialization being a tendency for enlargement of the incisors. These are very small animals, smaller than a rat, and show resemblances to the Insectivora.

As would be expected, the early forms of a major taxa are difficult to identify because

1. P. D. Gingerich, "Molar occlusion and jaw mechanics of the Eocene primate, *Adapis*," *American Journal of Physical Anthropology* 36 (1972): 359-368.

in such cases the identifying criteria for the extant representatives are lost, body size is usually small, and the frequency of specimens is low. All of these factors make for difficulty of interpretation so it should come as no surprise that no unanimous opinion exists concerning the interpretation of the Plesiadapiformes.

SUMMARY

The contemporary prosimians must be considered to be a fairly successful but primitive group of primates. As nocturnal forms from Asia and Africa, they are fairly common, and, on Madagascar and the Comoro Islands, they are the only primates. In their morphology they bridge the gap between the anthropoids and the Order Insectivora. When the fossil forms are considered, the link to the Insectivora is firmly established.

During the middle Cenozoic, prosimians are not well represented in the fossil record. Assuming that the record as known is representative of their frequency, their scarcity may be due to competition from either, or both, the rodents or the anthropoids who were becoming established during that time. If this is the case, it was probably during the middle Cenozoic that the prosimians invaded Madagascar, thus escaping competition, or took on their nocturnal habits, which relieved them from competition with anthropoids.

During the early Cenozoic all Orders of mammals were becoming established and were invading the niches left vacant by the reptiles. The development of many aberrant forms, as seen in the early prosimians, is also common in other mammalian Orders. Perhaps once the pressure from the reptiles was relieved, the mammals exploded into many ways of life. Many of these ways survived for a short time, only until less aberrant and more successfully adapted forms became established. Certainly the picture of early prosimians follows this same pattern seen elsewhere in the fossil record.

Classification of taxa discussed in chapter 7:

- Order: Primates
  - Suborder: Prosimii
    - Infraorder: Tarsiiformes
      - Superfamily: Tarsiioidea
        - Family: Tarsiidae
          - Subfamily: Tarsiinae
            - Genus: *Tarsius*—Recent (tarsier)
          - Subfamily: Microchoerinae—Eocene (4 Genera)
        - Family: Anaptomorphidae—Eocene-Miocene (22 Genera)
    - Infraorder: Lorisiformes
      - Superfamily: Lorisoidea
        - Family: Lorisidae
          - Subfamily: Galaginae
            - Genus: *Galago*—Recent (bush baby)
          - Subfamily: Lorisinae—Recent (loris, potto, 4 Genera)
            - Genera: *Indraloris*—Pliocene
              Progalago—Miocene
              Komba—Miocene
    - Infraorder: Lemuriformes
      - Superfamily: Lemuroidea
        - Family: Lemuridae—Pleistocene-Recent (16 Genera)
      - Superfamily: Adapoidea
        - Family: Adapidae
          - Subfamily: Adapinae—Eocene-Oligocene (7 Genera)
            Notharctinae—Eocene (3 Genera)
    - Infraorder: Plesiadapiformes
      - Family: Plesiadapidae—Paleocene-Eocene (5 Genera)
        Carpolestidae—Paleocene-Eocene (3 Genera)
        Paromomyidae—Creta-

ceous-Eocene (6 Genera)
Picrodontidae—Paleocene (2 Genera)

For Further Reading

Gingerich, P. D. "Cranial anatomy of the early Tertiary primates and the origin of the Anthropoidea." *American Journal of Physical Anthropology* 42 (1975):303.

McKenna, M. C. "Paleontology and the origin of the primates." *Folia primatologica* 4 (1966):1-25.

Van Valen, L. and R. E. Sloan. "The earliest primates." *Science* 150 (1965):743-745.

Bibliography

Gingerich, P. D. 1972. "Molar occlusion and jaw mechanics of the Eocene primate, *Adapis*." *American Journal of Physical Anthropology* 36:359-368.

8 The Primates: An Overview

In this final chapter we will take a general look at primate phylogeny. In the first chapter a list of primate traits applicable only to living forms was presented. It was noted that many authorities now feel that the single trait separating all Primates from nonprimate mammals is the structure of the floor of the middle ear, formed solely from the petrosal bone. This may be an excellent criterion, but unfortunately the earliest Genus recognized as being a primate, *Purgatorius* of the Cretaceous and Paleocene of North America, is known only from teeth. *Purgatorius* is placed in the Order Primates because its teeth closely resemble those of later Genera whose middle-ear structure is known. Whichever way one looks at these teeth their classification is tenuous.

However, these teeth emphasize several important points. First, the precise identification of the earliest members of any major taxon is extremely difficult. As one goes back in time to the beginning of any Order, the criteria used for identifying extant members are lost, and the species become more and more like the early members of other Orders. In the case of Order Primates, the early forms come to look like primitive members of the Order Insectivora (as do early members of the other Orders of the Class Mammalia). Such is the case with *Purgatorius.*

Secondly, this Genus is North American. In fact, of the 15 primate Genera from the Paleocene, 13 were found in what is now the United States. Today the only nonhuman primates native to North America are in southern Mexico, recent arrivals from South America. Thus the Primates seem to have differentiated from the Insectivora just prior to the opening of the Cenozoic. Furthermore, they seem to have made the differentiation in the northern part of the United States. Recent work on continental drift indicates that North America and Europe were still close together during Paleocene times and probably both were considerably south of their present latitude.

Of the 41 Genera known from the Eocene, 22 are North American; 15 are European; and four are Asiatic. During the Eocene the primates spread eastward, but so far as we know they were still restricted to the Northern Hemisphere. All Genera of the Paleocene and all but two from the Eocene are classified in the Suborder Prosimii.

A NEW EVOLUTIONARY SEQUENCE

The two exceptions are provisionally classified as Anthropoidea. These two Genera, *Amphipithecus* and *Pondaungia,* are placed in the Superfamily Hominoidea. If subsequent research should indicate that this provisional classification is correct, it would mean that the ancestors of man and his close relatives, the pongids, differentiated from the prosimian stock prior to the time at which monkeys become an identifiable group.

If one looks at the extant members of the Order Primates and assumes that man is the most highly evolved, then one can establish a sequence of forms leading from the primitive to the highly evolved. This sequence would be: prosimian → New World monkeys → Old World monkeys → apes → man. If the provisional placement of *Amphipithecus* and *Pondaungia* should turn out to be correct, however, this "logical" sequence would be phylogenetically incorrect.

From a small beginning in the Cretaceous the prosimians of the Paleocene and Eocene become a highly variable lot. Though unquestionably arboreal animals, there is some question about the type of food preferred by those who gave rise to the Anthropoidea. Cartmill feels that this initial adaptation was for an insectivorous diet.[1] The animal may have captured its prey by slow, well-coordinated movement along slender branches in the lower portions of the tropical forests. Such hunting would require acute color vision and an ability to accurately judge distances. Certainly this is the adaptation now seen in some of the Lorisiformes, but recall that this is the last Infraorder of the Prosimii to be identified in the fossil record.[2] Szalay has a different idea; he feels that the transition from insectivore to primate was brought about by an adaptation to the eating of fruits and leaves.[3] The dentition of many early Tertiary prosimians seems to indicate that this was their food preference.

Such discussions plus the difficulty of identifying the first primate emphasizes the point that selection is the principle guiding force for long-term evolution. Selection acts on a variable population by conferring reproductive advantage to that subgroup of individuals who have some behavioral distinction better suited to changing environmental situations. Such distinctions may be extremely difficult to identify from the fossil record.

Some time during the transition from Eocene to Oligocene, a change or reorganization took place in the Primates. Just what brought this about isn't clear, but it may have been due to increasing competition from the developing rodents. At least at about this time, most of the early Genera of prosimians become extinct. The prosimian record is very sparse until we find them diversified in their present locations.

AN ANTHROPOID RISE

At about this same time, Late Eocene or Early Oligocene, the Anthropoidea probably differentiated, and just as the prosimians, once established, rapidly spread into new areas, so too did the anthropoids. By Oligocene times anthropoids are found in the Fayum of Africa and in South America. It had been assumed that these South American primates had differentiated from North American prosimians and had migrated south. However, the recent studies of continental drift, showing that South America was still close to Africa at this time, and the resemblances between the Fayum primate *Apidium* and the early South American forms leads to the possibility that the platyrrhines came from Africa.

The primate fossil record in South America is very sparse and difficult to interpret. Part of that difficulty is due to our lack of

1. M. Cartmill, "Rethinking primate origins," *Science* 184 (1974):436-443.

2. D. Rackowski, "Primate evolution: Were traits selected for arboreal locomotion or visually directed predation?" *Science* 187 (1975):455-456.

3. F. S. Szalay, "The beginnings of primates," *Evolution* 22 (1968):19-36.

detailed knowledge of contemporary forms. These have not received the attention they deserve. The phylogeny of these primates must remain in a tenuous condition until more information is available.

It is unfortunate that our knowledge of Oligocene, Old World primates is so restricted to the Fayum of Egypt. It appears that this is a time of differentiation of monkeys, cercopithecids, and apes, pongids. The well-known Genus *Apidium* may be a key to this differentiation, but it occurred too late to have been the true common ancestor of these groups. *Apidium* may well be at the base of the cercopithecid line with its contemporaries *Aeolopithecus* leading to the hylobatids and *Aegyptopithecus* leading to the pongids.

If this is a reasonable reconstruction, *Aegyptopithecus* would have given rise to the dryopithecines of the Miocene, the time of maximum success of the pongids. Certainly since then they have decreased in frequency and geographical distribution. However, probably at about the opening of the Pliocene, they gave rise to a separate lineage which led to the australopithecines of Late Pliocene or Early Pleistocene. When some portion of the australopithecine population learned to manufacture tools, the human line became established.

At about this same time—the Pliocene—the cercopithecids began their differentiation and geographical expansion. Today they are a highly diverse group and, except where they come in direct competition with man, a very successful one.

SUMMARY

Such is a brief overview of the 65-million-year history of the Order Primates. It is a history of a relatively unspecialized, in a morphological sense, group of mammals. But they adapted to an arboreal mode of life with the retention and perfection of a highly flexible upper extremity. Development of the primate hand plus the shift from smell to sight as the primary sense were probably the two factors that permitted successful competition without overspecialization. Along with these two easily identifiable traits goes the development of the brain. Mammals generally put more emphasis on learned behavior than did their reptilian ancestors. But the Primates carried this emphasis on learning to its greatest development. Ultimately, this early established trend led to a species that depends for its very survival on learning; that species is of course *Homo sapiens*, or man.

Learning—with its final development, culture—is man's great specialization. Specializations in other animals have often led to their extinction. Let us hope that man can learn not to extinguish himself.

Bibliography

Cartmill, M. 1974. "Rethinking primate origins." *Science* 184:436-443.

Rackowski, D. 1975. "Primate evolution: Were traits selected for arboreal locomotion or visually directed predation?" *Science* 187: 455-456.

Szalay, F. S. 1968. "The beginnings of primates." *Evolution* 22:19-36.

Glossary

Abduction—Movement away from the center of the body.

Adduction—Movement toward the center of the body.

Arboreal—Living in the trees.

Biscuspid—Condition whereby a tooth has two cusps; applies principally to the premolars.

Bulla—An inflated expansion of bone; in the context of this book, expansion of the floor of the middle ear thereby enlarging the middle-ear cavity.

Caecum—The blind pouch at the beginning of the large intestine.

Calcarine Fissure—A fissure on the occipital lobe of the brain.

Canine Fossa—A depression in the maxillary bone just below the orbit and above the canine tooth.

Clavicle—The bony strut that connects the shoulder with the sternum or breast bone; the collar bone.

Condyle—The part of a bone that participates in the formation of a joint.

Cranium—That part of the head enclosing the brain; braincase.

Cusp—A small protrusion of enamel on the occlusal surface of a tooth.

Distal—A term applied to an extremity and referring to that part further from the center of the body.

Diurnal—Being active in daylight hours.

Ectotympanic—A bony ring that supports the tympanic membrane, or eardrum.

Extant—Still living; not extinct.

Extension—The straightening of a joint; for the shoulder joint, extension moves the upper extremity backwards.

Fibula—The more lateral of the two bones of the leg.

Fissure—A groove on the surface of an organ.

Flexion—The bending of a joint to produce an acute angle; for the shoulder joint, flexion moves the upper extremity forward.

Frontal Bone—The bone of the skull that forms the forehead.

Hallux—The innermost digit on the foot; the great toe.

Hypertrophied—An increase in size greater than expected on the basis of normal growth.

K/A—Designation of the absolute dating method whereby the decay of radioactive potassium to argon is used to establish an absolute age for a geologic strata.

Karyotypology—Study of the number, shape, and other characteristics of the chromosomes.

Leg—The segment of the lower extremity lying between the knee and the ankle.

Lumbar Region—That portion of the trunk below the ribs.

Mandible—The bone of the lower jaw.

Meatus—An opening; a canal.

Meatus, External Auditory—The canal extending from the external ear to the tympanic membrane.

Midsagittal Plane—An imaginary plane passing vertically through the skull or head in an anterior-posterior direction; it divides the skull or head into halves.

Nocturnal—Being active at night or during the early morning or late evening.

Nuchal Torus—A thickening of bone extending horizontally across the posterior portion of the skull; its development is proportional to the size of the nuchal (neck) musculature.

Occipital Condyles—The condyles on the occipital bone through which the weight of the head is passed to the vertebral column.

Occlusal Surface—The biting surface of a tooth.

Os Coxae—The bone on the lateral side of the hip that contains the hip joint; the hipbone.

Pentadactyly—The condition of having five digits.

Phylogeny—The course of change followed by a taxon through geologic time.

Plantigrade—A condition in which the palms of the hands and the soles of the feet are placed flat on the ground.

Postorbital Constriction—A condition in which the anterior portion of the frontal bone is narrower than the bony rim of the orbit; usually taken to indicate a lack of development of the frontal lobes of the brain.

Procumbent—At an angle from the vertical in an anterior direction.

Prognathism—A condition in which the face, or a portion thereof, projects beyond the anterior portion of the brain.

Pronation—Turning the palm in such a way that the bones of the forearm are crossed.

Proximal—A term applied to an extremity and referring to that part closer to the center of the body.

Quadrupedal—Walking on all four extremities.

Radius—The more lateral of the two bones of the forearm.

Ramus (pl. Rami)—A branch or projection; applied to a portion of a bone, blood vessel, or nerve.

Rotation—Movement of an extremity around its long axis.

Sacrum—A bone formed by the fusion of a number of vertebrae and which articulates with the two Os Coxae.

Scapula—A flat bone lying on the posterior surface of the chest and which, with the proximal bone of the upper extremity, forms the shoulder joint; the shoulder blade.

Sectorial—A shearing tooth.

Sexual Dimorphism—The condition where the two adult sexes of a species are recognizably different.

Supination—Turning the palm of the hand in such a manner that the bones of the forearm are parallel.

Taxon—Any unit in the classificatory system.

Thoracic Region—The portion of the trunk bearing ribs.

GLOSSARY
Continued

Tibia—The more medial of the two bones of the leg.

Tympanic Membrane—The eardrum.

Ulna—The more medial of the two bones of the forearm.

Index

INDEX
Continued